Through the Pages of History

Dedication

To my late father, Dr Andrew, who turned a reluctant reader into an avid one!

Acknowledgements

I thank Maureen Browne for publishing advice. Versions of some of these essays have appeared in *The Consultant* magazine. *Putting a Foot in It* was broadcast on RTÉ's *Sunday Miscellany* programme. Mary Kelleher and Yvonne O Mara typed some early drafts. Stephen O Connell gave technical advice, as did my daughter, Helen. Maureen O Donnell drew my attention to books by Rebecca Skloot and Michael Sheridan. I am especially indebted to my daughter, Michelle, who typed original versions of these essays. She has also shown unending patience and provided advice on layout and content. Finally, I thank Oscar Duggan for his belief, encouragement and editorial advice.

Contents

HeLa Cells

Henrietta Lacks: Unknowing Pioneer

Loretta Pleasant, later known as Henrietta Lacks, was born in Roanoke, Virginia. She died, aged 31, of metastatic cervical cancer. However, her cells live on as HeLa Cells, the first human cell line to be successfully reproduced long-term in laboratory conditions.

As an undergraduate, I had heard of HeLa Cells and been informed that they had originated from a lady called Helen Lake. The cell line was also variously referred to as originating from Helen L, Henrietta Lakes and Helen Larson but never Henrietta Lacks. It has been suggested that George Gey, who first grew the cells in culture, came up with a pseudonym to protect her identity. Conspiracy theorists believe the name Helen Lake suggested a Caucasian origin for the cell line. The confusion surrounding their origin persisted for twenty-one years until 1973. The reason her name in real life morphed from Loretta to Henrietta is unknown. Her mother was Elisa Lacks Pleasant, which may explain the change of surname. While her eponymous HeLa cell line became and remains justifiably famous among medical researchers, Henrietta herself has been largely unknown.

After her mother's death, Henrietta and her nine siblings were sent to live with relatives. At age 4, she was taken in by her grandfather, who was already rearing another grandchild called David (Day), who was then aged 9. David and Henrietta grew up together sharing a bedroom. She was just 14 when she had their first child, a son and four years later, she had a daughter. They married when she was 20 and Day was 25 in 1941. They made a subsistence living growing tobacco. She later moved to Baltimore when Day found a job with Bethlehem Steel.

She had three more children and four months after her last pregnancy, presented at Johns Hopkins Hospital with vaginal bleeding. She was known to have Neurosyphilis and Gonorrhoea but had failed to attend for treatment. A large cervical mass was found and surgical sections were taken. A week later she was told that the biopsies showed a malignancy and she was recalled for radium treatment. Prior to inserting the radium, two wedge biopsies were taken from her cervix and some of this tissue was sent to George Gey's Cell Culture laboratory. Gey called cell lines he was attempting to grow by the first two letters of the donor Christian and surname. Thus, the cells were labelled HeLa.

The profuse bleeding had forced Henrietta to seek hospital care. That she did so with reluctance must be put into context. Johns Hopkins had specified in his bequest, setting up the medical school and charity hospital in Baltimore, that it be open to all including the indigent sick regardless of sex, age or colour. Despite this, the black community still viewed it with suspicion. It was rumoured that it had been set up in the poor area of Baltimore to enable easy recruitment of African Americans for use in research. There was an urban myth about supposed abduction of blacks by "Night Doctors" for this purpose. Word had also leaked out about the scandalous Tuskegee Study of Syphilis on African Americans.

The concept of fully informed consent did not exist in the 1950s and Henrietta signed an open permission before her initial examination and treatment. Not only was she unaware that attempts were being made to culture her cells but, she did not understand that radium treatment of her cancer would render her infertile. She was just 31 years of age when she died.

By the time of her death, her cell line was established. Unlike all previous lines, it did not die off after a few days. Indeed, it proliferated in culture medium. The impetus for mass production for HeLa cells came from the necessity to test the newly developed Salk Inactivated Polio Vaccine. HeLa cells were infected with polio virus and exposed to serum from vaccinated children to prove the vaccine effective. Her cells were later grown on an industrial scale and became central to much viral and tumour research.

Henrietta's children had known nothing of the growth of their mother's cells until 20 years after this had begun. While nothing illegal was done in the way the tissue was used, the family were resentful that they had been kept unaware of the use of their mother's tissue in research. Henrietta's husband came to believe that the cell line had made huge profits for Hopkins (it had not). The extended family, living in semi-poverty, felt cheated. Henrietta's eldest daughter, who was mentally handicapped, deaf and dumb, was put into care when Henrietta had her last baby. She was placed in Crownsville, a hospital formerly known as "the hospital for the Negro insane". She only outlived her mother by four years, dying aged 15.

Sadly, Henrietta lies in an unmarked grave near the family home in Virginia. Her lasting memorial is the cell line grown from her cervical cancer, which has proved invaluable in medical science. Rebecca Skloot's recent biography details the life of this unknowing pioneer. It addresses the problems of consanguinity, sexually transmitted disease, crime and drug use common in Henrietta' social group.

As an Intern in Johns Hopkins in the early 1960's the author has no recall of any attempt to correct the incorrect attribution of the cell line to a non-existent Helen Lake. George Gey died in 1970. A tribute article written by Howard Jones (the gynaecologist who treated Henrietta) and Victor McKusick (a geneticist) appeared the following year. In this, they referred to Henrietta Lacks as the source of the He La cell line. Nevertheless, it was 1973 before the controversy was put to rest when both Jones and McKusick publicly set the record straight. Henrietta has eventually been honoured when Johns Hopkins instituted the annual Henrietta

Lacks memorial lectures. The woman whose cell line was vital to development of inactivated Polio vaccine, whose cells have travelled to outer space and have been exposed to nuclear radiation has finally, like her cell line, become immortal.

Further Reading

The Immortal Life of Henrietta Lacks by Rebecca Skloot (Crown Publishers, New York. 2010)

Saul Krugman

Willowbrook Hepatitis Experiments

"The most unethical experiments ever performed on children in the United States." – **Maurice Hillman**

Saul Krugman, an American paediatrician and researcher into vaccines, carried out a series of experimental hepatitis studies on mentally disabled children in Willowbrook State School, in Staten Island, New York, from the mid-1950s to 1964. The studies were approved by the New York State Department of Mental Hygiene and the Epidemiological Board of the Office of Surgeon General. Huge epidemics of hepatitis had occurred during the American Civil War as well as the First and Second World Wars. American forces were supportive of any study that might lead to better understanding of the disease and, ideally, one that might lead to development of a vaccine.

Krugman's co-workers included his Yale colleague, Robert McCollum, Joan Giles and Jack Hammond, the Chief Medical Officer in Willowbrook. At the time, there was no animal model. Tissue culture was, as yet, unavailable so, experiments had to be carried out on humans.

The studies identified two types of infectious hepatitis. Hepatitis A had a short incubation period and abnormal transaminase blood levels for three to 19 days. It was transmitted by the faecal oral route. Hepatitis B had an incubation period of 41 to 108 days and blood transaminase levels remained elevated for 35 to 200 days.

Among the first public critics of these experiments was Senator Samuel Thaler in the early 1960s. Maurice Hillman, who was the foremost worker in the introduction and development of human vaccines, was strident in his condemnation of the Willowbrook experiments. Dr Henry Beecher included them in a paper, outlining studies he considered unethical in the *New England Journal of Medicine*, in 1966 and expanded on them in a book in 1970.

Construction began, in Willowbrook in 1938, of a facility to cater for children with intellectual disability. At the time, it was believed that such children would benefit from institutional care. However, when it was completed in 1942, it was used as a hospital by the US armed forces. After World War II, the initial plan was to hand it over to the Veterans' Administration. This did not proceed and in 1947, it opened, as originally planned, as a facility for children with intellectual disability, under the control of the New York State Department of Mental Hygiene.

Saul Krugman was appointed Consultant in Infectious Disease to Willowbrook in 1954. In 1967, Krugman stated, "Willowbrook was not chosen because its population is mentally retarded, but because it had endemic infectious hepatitis and a sufficiently open population, so that the disease (hepatitis) could never be quieted by exhausting the supply of susceptibles."

As adult staff members also contracted hepatitis (resulting in an average loss of 60 working days for those affected) it is hard to understand why no adults were recruited into the studies.

The viral aetiology of infectious hepatitis was only finally proven by human experimentation during the Second World War. Multiple attempts to isolate a causative bacterium had failed. Voigt in Germany demonstrated the first transmission between human volunteers. Cameron, working with British Forces in the Palestine Mandate, in the early 1940s, injected six adult volunteers with infected blood. All six, developed hepatitis. Human volunteers with rheumatoid disease developed hepatitis having been fed faecal material obtained from infected British soldiers. Further volunteer studies were carried out in conscientious objectors and prisoners. There were still many unanswered questions surrounding infectious hepatitis, however and Krugman's experiments were designed to attempt to unravel them.

It must be acknowledged that the work proved invaluable, by establishing the existence of two distinct viruses. Derived from the initialism of the child's name from which the infected material emanated, they were named MS1, short incubation "infectious" hepatitis and MS2, long incubation "serum" hepatitis. He proved there was no cross immunity between MS1 and MS2. MS1 was spread exclusively by the faecal oral route whereas MS2 was spread almost exclusively by body fluids and sexual contact.

Prior to commencing his experiments on children, Krugman did an epidemiological study in Willowbrook, surveying the water supply sewage and food. He showed that the source of infection was contact with infected fellow students. The strain of virus was mild. There were no hepatitis-related deaths in children or staff between 1953 and 1957.

Stokes, in Pennsylvania, had shown that gamma globulin could modify the course of the disease and postulated that if given at the correct time, might confer immunity. Krugman thought that infection with even a mild strain could lead to long-term immunity. In studies that went on for 15 years, he fed infected stools in milk shakes to one cohort and not to a control group. Varying doses of gamma globulin were administered to try and induce immunity.

The studies were performed in a separate hepatitis unit, to protect the study group from other communicable diseases common in the institution. No child was entered into a study without the consent of parents or guardians. A pro-forma letter, outlining the research study and asking parents to sign consent if they wished their child included, was sent to all parents of new admissions. Initially, Dr Joan Giles met parents in groups but later, they were invited to see the facility and question researchers.

Willowbrook was designed to house a maximum of 4000 children but had a population of 6000 when Krugman joined the staff. Hepatitis was rampant. It was said that almost all newly admitted children would contract hepatitis in the first six to twelve months. Krugman argued that by administering a controlled infective dose, the children would be no worse off than if left to contract it naturally and, indeed, their disease course did appear milder. He did, however, inflate the risk to newcomers. The true risk was probably 30 to 50%. Children fed infected stool had a 100% infection rate.

At one stage, in 1964, the chronic overcrowding became so severe that admissions were halted. Some weeks later, Dr Jack Hammond wrote to parents with children on the waiting list to say that some places were now vacant in the hepatitis unit. Only children entering the research programme were eligible for such admission and this is seen as a form of coercion.

In favour of the studies, it is argued that benefit outweighed potential harm. Because hepatitis was rampant, those artificially infected were not at excessive risk. The research yielded valuable information on the aetiology of the infecting viruses. Material gathered led to the first effective vaccine. As they were housed in a special facility the children were protected from other endemic disease in the main blocks. Isolation of infected children in general was considered impractical.

State, university and federal review boards approved the protocols. Those against point to the inability of these vulnerable children to comprehend potential risks. Feeding live hepatitis virus to mentally disabled children disrespected their basic human rights. They question whether parents were fully informed of the short or long-term risks. They believe that admission to a well-equipped new facility was an undue inducement.

The Helsinki Declaration now states, "there is no right to risk injury to one person for the benefit of others."

Krugman's critics say that he exploited a bad situation rather than attempting to remedy it. There was no reason to confine the study to children yet, no adults were enrolled, even though attendants ran similar risks of becoming infected in the unsanitary conditions prevailing outside the hepatitis unit.

By 1965, the hepatitis studies had been discontinued but not before some staff resigned in protest at the experiments. At least one whistle blower had her contract terminated. When Robert Kennedy visited, in 1965, he described the institution as a "snake pit". He observed the children "were living in filth and dirt, their clothing in rags, in rooms less comfortable than the cages we put animals in a zoo."

In 1972, Geraldo Rivera gained access to one unit, being let in by a Dr Walters, who had been dismissed for trying to organise parents to push for improvements. Rivera made a shocking video, which is available on YouTube. He has also followed up by investigating physical and sexual abuse inflicted by staff on the children, in this and like institutes.

Saul Krugman died, aged 84 years, in 1995. He left a mixed legacy. He contributed greatly to our understanding of viral hepatitis. He identified two distinct viruses causing the disease: MS1 (hepatitis A) and MS2 (hepatitis B). He demonstrated their modes of transmission. Building on his work, the hepatitis viruses have been isolated and preventive vaccines developed. He became President of the American Paediatric Association in 1972. He was awarded a Lascar award (sometimes called the American Nobels) in 1983.

While the Willowbrook hepatitis experiments do not rank with the infamous Tuskegee syphilis study, or the Chester Southam cancer experiments in the Brooklyn Jewish Chronic Hospital, they would not receive ethical approval today. By deliberately infecting children, he increased their rate of infection to 100%. There was associated morbidity if not mortality. While it is probable that those exposed to MS1 did not develop chronic liver damage, no such claim can be advanced for those exposed to MS2.

Yellow Fever

Its Role in the Building of the Panama Canal

The narrow landmass linking North and South America excited the imagination of early explorers as to the possibility of creating an inter-oceanic canal. Various possible routes across the isthmus were proposed. Finally, it appeared that the most promising ones were across Panama (then part of Colombia) or Nicaragua. The French favoured the Panama route and the US, that through Nicaragua.

Ferdinand de Lesseps, a French diplomat, had masterminded the building of the Suez Canal, linking the Mediterranean and the Red Sea. This took 10 years to build, opening in 1869. It is a sea level, lockless canal. After the success of the Suez Canal, the French were confident that they could construct a similar lockless canal across the Panama Isthmus and obtained the necessary permission, by treaty, from Colombia to carry out its construction.

An international company was set up, with de Lesseps at its head. He believed that this inter-oceanic canal could also be built as a sea level canal. He predicted it could be built in less than the 10 years it took to construct the Suez Canal. However, de Lesseps was a diplomat and not an engineer. The Suez was essentially a large ditch cut into the desert. The Panama Canal would have to deal with excavating through the rocky spine of Central America. With the charismatic de Lesseps heading it up however, the company raised huge amounts of capital, especially in France. That the French attempt ultimately failed was only in part due to technical problems encountered but also, largely due to the burden of illness suffered by those attempting to construct the canal.

Yellow Fever

This was first recorded along the west coast of Africa. The disease was carried by slave traders to the Caribbean and Latin America, where it was widespread by the 1700s. It is said to have killed one third of the population of Cuba and Barbados. Outbreaks occurred in Colombia, Peru, New Orleans and up the east coast of North America as far as Boston. Europe, with few exceptions, escaped the disease. Infected ships were quarantined and required to fly a flag called "the Yellow Jack", by which name the disease also became known.

Quarantine assumed that the disease was contagious. This view was strenuously opposed by many in the medical profession, who considered that it was the result of heat effects on putrefied material and dead animals – so called 'miasma'. Quarantine had a devastating effect on trade and it was no surprise that commercial interests strongly promoted the miasmic theories, as opposed to contagion.

Yellow fever presents with headache, anorexia, muscle pain followed by profound thirst and excruciating backache. Next comes fever, jaundice and then liver, kidney and multiple organ failure with coma. One of the most dreaded clinical symptoms in Panama was bloody vomit; the so-called 'Vomito Negro'. Such vomiting usually presaged a fatal outcome.

In the early 1800s, John Crawford postulated a role for mosquitoes in its transmission. Others made similar claims but, evidence was lacking. Carlos Finlay, a Cuban physician, postulated that a specific species of mosquito (Aedes aegypti) might transmit the disease, having bitten a yellow fever patient. Finlay embarked on a number of experiments, attempting to prove the transmissible nature of the disease but failed to convince his medical peers.

Confusingly, in 1897, an Italian bacteriologist claimed to have isolated the bacteria responsible for the disease. Following huge mortality of US troops in the Spanish-American War and a big epidemic in Cuba, the US Army Yellow Fever Commission was constituted in 1900. Walter Reed and James Carroll headed this up. The commission's belief in the disease being transferred by a vector was bolstered by the work of Ronald Ross in India who, in 1897, had shown that the Anopheles mosquito transmitted malaria.

As there was no known animal infected, Reed and Carroll had to do their experiments on humans, including themselves. The crucial experiment involved soldier volunteers. These men were offered a monetary incentive but, they all declined it. One group lived exposed to bedding used by victims (so called fomites) and the second group were isolated and exposed to potentially infected mosquitoes that had bitten yellow fever victims. None of the first group contracted the disease, but 80% of the second group did. Fortunately, none died. The commission concluded that mosquitoes transmitted the disease and the agent was so small, it could pass through filters that retained the smallest known bacteria.

William Gorgas in Cuba followed these findings up. He set out to eliminate breeding sites of mosquitoes. Within months, the disease was eliminated in Havana. Gorgas was to play a major part in its ultimate control in Panama but, even the success of his work in Cuba was insufficient to convince others of the importance of eliminating the mosquito vector.

Panama Canal Construction
The Germans, French, Americans and British all had competing hopes of constructing an inter-oceanic canal between the Pacific and Atlantic. The United States favoured the Nicaraguan route and judged the Panama route impractical. Treaty negotiations were begun with Nicaragua, with a view to securing access to construct a canal.

The public appetite in North America was for a US controlled canal, rather than an international one controlled on a model of the Suez Canal. It came as a shock to the US public when, in May 1879, it was announced that the International Congress had approved the building of the canal located in Panama, to be built by the French! Reaction in the US varied from outrage to dismay at what was seen as a flouting of the Monroe Doctrine.

Soon, de Lessep set about raising four hundred million francs start-up money. In February 1881, he triumphantly read out a telegram to the French press – *Travail Commence* (the work is begun). Illness, climatic factors, graft and ultimately, financial disaster ended the initial attempt in 1889. A new company was formed in 1894 but the project proved beyond it and the work ceased.

The US Senate, in the meantime, had authorised monies for the building of a rival canal in Nicaragua, which caused panic in France. The New Canal Company offered to sell out to the US for forty million dollars. By a slim margin of 8 votes, the US senate gave its backing to the deal. However, the Colombians would not agree to transfer ownership to the US. President Teddy Roosevelt backed a nationalist rebellion and Panama declared itself a republic. A subsequent treaty gave the US absolute control over the future canal and surrounding Canal Zone. Despite monumental odds, the project was completed as a lock canal and opened in 1914.

Yellow Fever in Panama

William Gorgas, who had controlled yellow fever in Cuba, was part of a US team deployed to oversee continued work on the canal. Despite his work in Cuba, Gorgas got little support from the newly formed Commission in Panama. Indeed, the American Chief Engineer, Wallace, described the Mosquito Vector Theory as "balderdash" and the Zone Governor, Davis told Gorgas patronisingly, "Yellow fever as we all know is caused by filth."

Gorgas' task was magnified by the fact that in Panama, the mosquito breeds all year round as opposed to only in the rainy season in Cuba. Requisitioned medical and allied equipment was delayed and deferred and even the resident Americans proved uncooperative to Gorgas, like propping open screened doors designed to keep mosquitoes at bay.

Death and resignations prompted Washington to send Dr Charles Reed on a commission of inspection. Its leaked report infuriated Roosevelt, with his documentation of excessive red tape. The commission had now been reduced to three men: Wallace, the chief engineer; Shouts, the chairman and Magoon, the new Governor. They sought to have Gorgas replaced by a "more practical doctor". Taft, the Secretary of War agreed. Having taken medical advice from a hunting companion, Roosevelt took the bold step of overruling Taft and ordered Magoon to give Gorgas all he requested.

In July 1905, Gorgas commenced his full-on sanitary campaign. He recruited local doctors to help in eliminating breeding sites of the mosquito. Residences from the grandest to the poorest were fumigated. Paper strips were used to seal windows, doors and any cracks from which mosquitoes could escape. Fetid water that could not be drained was sprayed with kerosene. Running water was introduced. He even had the holy water in the cathedral font changed daily, having found it contaminated with breeding larvae. Fresh water traps were set up daily as the female Anopheles mosquito favoured clean water to lay its eggs. These larvae were then destroyed each day. High-grade copper screens were installed in every American home. Hospital facilities were greatly expanded. Gorgas' department spent fifty thousand dollars in the first year and two million in the second, but it worked! The last case of yellow fever in Panama City occurred in November 1905.

While other causes of fever, such as malaria, killed more during the canal project, none was so feared as yellow fever. This was particularly so among whites and with good reason. Many of the low paid labourers came from Jamaica and Barbados and, due to previous exposure, were immune to yellow fever. The white managing class, by contrast, were far more prone to infection. There were many poignant deaths. The 18-year-old daughter of a French director general died of yellow fever, as did her brother and her fiancée. An American newspaper called Panama "the place where the double ghost walks."

The corner was finally turned when William Gorgas was given full backing to eliminate the Aedes aegypti mosquito. To this doctor, son of a Confederate general, goes the credit of eliminating yellow fever from Panama.

De Lesseps had predicted the canal would be built by 1888. In fact, it ultimately took 23 years to complete. Sadly, de Lesseps final years were clouded with scandal and disgrace. The Americans finally completed the canal, which opened on the 15th August 1914. Unlike the celebration surrounding the opening of the Suez Canal, which included Verdi's opera, *Aida*, the Panama Canal opened with little ceremony. One of the greatest engineering feats ever carried out by mankind found news of its opening confined to the inner pages of the major newspapers, pushed aside by the outbreak of the Great War in Europe.

Further Reading
Hell's Gorge: The Battle to Build the Panama Canal by Mathew Parker (Arrow Books. 2008)

The Greatest Benefit to Mankind by Roy Porter (Harper Collins. 1997)

Poliomyelitis

Cork: The Last Major Epidemic in Europe

Poliomyelitis probably existed in ancient Egypt as early as 3700 BC. A later funerary stelae shows a figure with a wasted leg and equinus deformity, which many think represents the first graphic evidence of polio.

There are three strains of poliomyelitis virus. Fortunately, Type 2 appears to have been successfully eradicated worldwide.

Type 1 (Brunhilde) is the strain associated with the majority of worldwide epidemics, which peaked in the early 1950s. This caused the polio epidemic in Cork in 1956. The associated panic in the community can only be compared to that when AIDS first appeared. Farmers with a family member affected found their milk churns were not collected and neighbours crossed muddy fields rather than walk the road by their houses. Indignant letters poured into the office of the Minister of Health (T.F. O'Higgins), for allowing Cork hurling fans to travel to Croke Park, with the implied risk of infecting the people of Dublin. (Polio also occurred in Dublin that year but not in epidemic numbers).

In his book, *The Broken Boy*, Patrick Cockburn quotes Department of Health sources stating that there were 220 diagnosed cases in Cork out of a total of 499 in Ireland, with 20 deaths that year. This suggests that upwards of 50,000 people were attacked by the virus but, most attacks resulted in sub-clinical illness.

Ironically and tragically, the epidemic in Cork came a year too early for the Salk vaccine, which was already being trialled in the United States. The Cork epidemic was the last major one in Western Europe. As a pre-clinical student in UCC, I recall the epidemic vividly and, in particular, the iron lungs in the Cork Fever Hospital supplied by the Nuffield Trust.

Epidemiologically, poliomyelitis appeared baffling. It did not behave like other infectious diseases, such as typhus and cholera, which were synonymous with poor hygiene. On the contrary, polio broke barriers and appeared to attack the affluent. As countries developed higher standards of living and improved hygiene, polio moved from a relatively mild public health problem – "infantile paralysis" – to the epidemic disease that, at its height, saw 50,000 of all ages affected in the summer months in the United States of America.

These epidemics arose as a result of diminished herd immunity. Studies in Scotland, in 1955-56, showed that children in social grades 3-5 (the more affluent groups) acquired antibodies more rapidly and completely in early childhood than those in economically poorer grades 1 and 2. In the Cork epidemic, this was reflected in the preponderance of cases occurring in middle class suburbs and led to distracted mothers asking public health officials, should they expose their children to more dirt!

The polio virus shares with smallpox and measles the lack of an animal reservoir. The presence of an effective vaccine has led to the elimination of smallpox worldwide. Why then has it proved so difficult to eliminate poliomyelitis as effective vaccines exist? The answer is complex. Elimination depends on the development of community or herd immunity. Not all immunised persons develop immunity to polio. About 95% of those immunised become immune and it takes 80% population immunity to provide herd immunity.

Two effective vaccines exist: Inactivated Polio Vaccine (IPV) developed by Salk and Oral Polio Vaccine (OPV) developed by Sabin. The preferred vaccine in developed countries is Trivalent IPV. It is effective and never causes vaccine associated polio. OPV remains the WHO preferred vaccine in developing countries because of cost and ease of administration. It does, however, cause polio very rarely (estimated risk one in 2.5 million) and can also cause polio as a result of exposure to mutated savant strains, where there is low background immunity.

Franklin Delano Roosevelt (FDR), the 32nd President of the USA, contracted polio in 1921, at the age of 39. He was left with wasted, weakened lower limbs and needed steel callipers to stand and walk. Despite this, he became Governor of New York State and, in 1932, President of the USA.

While he spoke openly of his illness, he was careful to project his public image as physically able. Indeed, only two photographs are known to exist of him in a wheelchair. Initially, he refused to accept the medical prognosis and, hearing of the healing powers of thermal springs, sought rehabilitation in Warm Springs, Georgia. Pleased with his therapy, he bought the resort and later set up a foundation catering for polio victims' rehabilitation there – though, it remained "Whites only" in his lifetime.

Keen to support research into polio, he set up the President's Birthday Ball Commission and later, the incredibly successful (financially) March of Dimes. The financial assistance to research polio proved vital to the ultimate development of vaccines.

FDR's health declined rapidly during World War II and, by 1944, his deterioration was blamed on cigarette smoking, hypertension and ischaemic heart disease. In retrospect, it seems likely that he also suffered post-polio syndrome, resulting in severe fatigue and progressive further weakness in his lower limbs. It is difficult to overestimate the importance of his long-term contribution to the eradication of the disease.

Global Polio Eradication

In 1985, Rotary International pledged to raise 120 million dollars towards eradication of the disease by worldwide immunisation. To date, Rotary International worldwide continues to provide funds toward this aim on an annual basis. The global polio eradication initiatives saw the World Health Organisation join with Rotary International and others, with the aim of eliminating the disease by the year 2000. Sadly, that was not achieved but, huge positives have emerged.

In 2012, India, formerly a huge contributor to the burden of this disease, reported its first year free of paralytic polio. Epidemic polio now exists in three countries: Pakistan, Afghanistan and Nigeria. However, since 2003, 18 countries previously polio free have reported outbreaks due to importation or re-established transmission. Many of the difficulties in the final push to eradicate polio are highlighted in a *Lancet* editorial (5 January 2013).

In 2003, the immunisation programme was suspended in the state of Kano, Nigeria as a result of widespread misinformation, leading people there to believe that it caused sterility in females and AIDS. Not only did polio rebound in Nigeria during the 10 months suspension of immunisation but it spread to 15 other African countries, formerly polio free. Recently, there have been further killings of health workers administering the vaccine in Kano, which have been blamed on the Islamist militant group, Boko Haram. This group also have expressed determination to impose Sharia Law in Nigeria.

In Pakistan, nine health workers were shot dead in December 2012 and in January 2013, six female aid workers and a male doctor were killed. As a result, the vaccination programme has been temporarily halted by the government of Pakistan. In June 2012, the Taliban announced a ban on immunisation in retaliation for the use of unmanned drones by the USA against Taliban targets in Pakistan. It is estimated that more than 3.5 million children have now missed vaccination as a result of its suspension in that country.

The preponderance of female aid workers killed is a result of the cultural fact that, in Pakistan, only women are allowed to enter homes, talk to the mothers and administer vaccines. After the Twin Towers attack, rumours became widespread in Pakistan that polio immunisation causes sterility. Attempts to counteract this misinformation have not been helped by the CIA's fake Hepatitis B immunisation campaign in Abbottabad, designed to confirm Osama bin Laden's presence there by checking DNA samples taken from his children.

Post-Polio Syndrome

While it has long been recognised that modest decrease in muscle power occurs with age, in those suffering from paralytic poliomyelitis, it is now clear that some victims develop a specific syndrome – post-polio syndrome (PPS) – decades after the initial paralysis. While the cause is unknown, failure of re-innervated motor units, auto-immune damage and possible persistence of the polio virus have been postulated. The severity of initial paralysis seems to predispose suffers to PPS. Those who contracted polio as adolescents or adults are more prone, as are those who made the greatest initial recovery from the illness.

The principal physical manifestation is muscle weakness. To fulfil the criteria for PPS, this must occur in an identified polio victim and appear at least 15 years after the initial diagnosis and, the weakness must last at least one year, in the absence of other possible causes. Generalised fatigue is also common. Other features include muscle pain and, more seriously but less often, respiratory abnormalities.

Much done, more to do

Despite setbacks, much has been achieved. Type 2 poliomyelitis appears to have been eliminated. Currently, only three countries (Nigeria, Pakistan and Afghanistan) have endemic disease. India became polio free in 2012. Recorded cases have fallen from 52,000 in 1980 to 89 in 2012. The vaccine of choice is Trivalent Inactivated Polio Vaccine. For reasons of cost and administration, Oral Polio Vaccine is still recommended by WHO for developing countries.

The Black Death

Historical and Medical Perspectives

Reminders of the Black Death in the Cork of my youth were the metal rat plates fitted to the hawsers, securing ships to the docks. When I returned as a Consultant Physician, my first ward sister was Sr Roch, named after the saint invoked against plague. We also believed that the nursery rhyme "Ring a Ring o' Roses" referred to plague, although this is now disputed.

Plague, from the Latin, *plaga* (a blow) has come to be used indiscriminately for any rapidly spreading, frequently fatal disease. In its strictest medical usage, it refers to infection with bacillus *Yersinia pestis*.

There have been three major pandemics of plague, all originated in China. The first was the "Justinian Plague", in the Eastern Roman Empire in the 6th and 7th century and the third occurred in the 19th century. The second and most devastating pandemic occurred in the 14th century and it is this that is referred to as "The Black Death". It almost certainly spread by trader's travelling the silk route, entering Europe via the Crimea. It then spread overland and by sea to major ports in Europe. It flared intermittently over the next three centuries, killing up to one million people worldwide (a quarter of the world's population at the time). Weather conditions, war and famine contributed to its spread. The term, black, may refer to the skin's discolouration, due to intravascular coagulation and gangrene. It may alternatively refer to the dire mood induced by the ravages of the disease.

Since the 1970s, some scientists have challenged the central role of *Yersinia pestis* in this pandemic. Sceptics have focussed on the rapid spread in this era of primitive slow transport, the high mortality, high rat death rates and the cold temperatures in Europe not being conducive to flea survival. However, there are no reports of plague outbursts in severe winters. Undoubtedly, coexistent illness, such a typhus, smallpox, dysentery and anthrax contributed to overall mortality. An Ebola type viral illness has also been suggested. Most of these sceptical analyses omit consideration of the human-to-human transmission by the pneumonic variety. DNA and protein signature analysis of human remains from plague pits around Europe now appear to have conclusively proven that *Yersinia pestis* was the prime, constant agent causing The Black Death. Now extinct clades of the *Yersinia pestis* genome also existed at that time.

"Flee early, flee far, return late." This was the general advice given when plague approached. On the other hand, it was known that such flight could spread the disease if those fleeing were infected, leading most city states to bring in some form of quarantine for victims.

Michelangelo Merisi was already in his home town of Caravaggio, east of Milan, when plague struck that city. His grandfather and father fled Milan for Caravaggio but were already infected. Not only did they die but they contributed to the spread of the disease in their home town. Michelangelo survived and became the painter eponymously known as "Caravaggio".

Another survivor was the infant, William Shakespeare. One quarter of the population of Stratford-upon-Avon died of the plague, including all of the children of one family in the street where Shakespeare lived. He later escaped death from a further outbreak, when living in London as a playwright.

While the medical profession still largely accepted it was spread by "miasma", it was generally recognised that quarantine of sufferers helped limit the spread. Indeed, sufferers were frequently abandoned by surviving family members and left to die alone, unattended and unfed. Only clerics and plague doctors would visit such homes. The classic, spine-chilling symbol was the red cross painted in oil on the door of the victim's house.

While the rich were able to stay ahead of an outbreak by travelling to distant country houses, not all the nobility escaped. The Black Death was sweeping Europe when the Plantagenet King Edward III arranged a dynastic wedding between his 15-year-old second daughter Joan and Peter son of Alfonso XI of Castile. The Plague had not yet reached England when she sailed from Portsmouth in August 1348 in a convoy of four ships. On board, was a magnificent red silk wedding bed and a wedding dress made from 450 feet of silk, interwoven with gold thread. When the convoy approached Bordeaux, the Mayor sent out a warning the plague had broken out in the city. Her advisors ignored the warning and she disembarked, with the intention of travelling overland to Castile. By mid-August, her chief advisor, a veteran of Crécy, was dead and Princess Joan died of plague on 2 September. She never got to wear her wedding dress or meet her intended spouse.

Panic and religious fanaticism led to the scapegoating of groups perceived as responsible for sins, leading to this divinely sent disaster. Lepers and sufferers from skin disease or disease such as acne and psoriasis were targeted and often murdered.

Medieval Christians believed that Jews poisoned wells, desecrated the divine host and even carried out human sacrifice of Christian children. So, despite suffering similar mortality to their fellow Christians, they were persecuted throughout continental Europe (Jews had been expelled from England in 1290 by Edward I) and hundreds of Jewish communities were wiped out. Many of these killings took place despite the intervention of Pope Clement VI, who issued two papal bulls condemning the killings and instructing Christians to be tolerant and restrained, even stating that continued persecution of Jews would lead to excommunication.

Clement believed, however, that plague was sent by God to punish evil. He organised processions of penitents, fasting and praying. An extreme group of penitents practised self-flagellation. Clement initially took part in these processions but, realising they might contribute to the spread of the disease, he later banned them. He specifically forbade the practice of bands of flagellants wandering from town to town, spreading panic and disease.

For a Pope who prided himself on his taste for beautiful women and exotic clothes and had no fewer than three thousand guests at his coronation banquet, he proved remarkably brave when the Black Death ravaged Avignon. Not only did he not flee the city, he arranged for the dead to be buried and gave general absolution. He bought a large field, which was converted to a badly needed extra cemetery as up to three quarters of the local population died in the outbreak. He did withdraw to his private apartments and sat wrapped in blankets between two constantly blazing fires. Clement VI was the first Pope to attempt active defence of the Jewish community.

A Zoonosis

Plague is a zoonosis; the classic host is *Rattus rattus*, the black or ship rat. Infected rats survive some weeks whereas other host species die very rapidly. Rattus rattus originated in India and was introduced to England by the Romans. Smaller than the brown or sewer rat (Rattus norvegicus), it has a long tail and is an excellent tree climber. Plague can also infect the brown rat. Other species acting as carriers include squirrels, wood rats, gerbils, dogs, cats, chipmunks, marmots, camels, mice, voles, prairie dogs and humans.

Plague is transmitted by fleas or direct contact. Xenopsylla cheopis, the oriental rat flea, which is the primary vector, must be within hopping distance of its target. However, as fleas can survive for up to six months, transmission can occur even after the infected animal is dead. In the human, the incubation period is six days. Plague manifests as fever, dyspnoea and ecchymosis due to internal bleeding. Next, egg-sized swellings (buboes) appear in the lymph nodes of the neck, groin and armpit. Three clinical forms exist: septicaemic, pneumonic and bubonic. There is some evidence that the pneumonic form was common in the outbreaks of the Middle Ages.

Reservoirs of the disease exist on every continent except Australia. Stanseth et al of Oslo University have addressed the explanation of persistent outbreaks in Europe over four centuries after the second plague pandemic of 1347-1353. They postulate repeated reintroduction of the plague bacterium including via the Asia gerbil. It is suggested that climate driven boom and bust of such host populations in Asia may have led to repeated introduction of the bacteria to Europe via the silk route by fleas on camels or human vectors. Despite misleading news headlines, they never suggested the Asian gerbil rather than the black rat was the main flea vector in Europe. Rather they questioned the persistence of European rodent plague reservoirs in the rat.

Outbreaks in Ireland

Plague arrived in Ireland in 1348. It came a month after it broke out in Bristol, probably introduced by a ship from Bordeaux. The big ports of Dublin and Drogheda were affected, followed by Waterford, Youghal and Cork. It took its biggest toll on the Anglo-Norman inhabitants of these towns. The rural Gaelic population was more scattered and lesser mortality occurred in this group.

Documentation is limited but a friar, John Clyn, a Franciscan monk in Kilkenny noted that visiting the sick and burying the dead was no longer universally performed. He described the bubonic and pneumonic forms before dying of the disease himself. The risk to compliant clergy is evident in Clyn's observation that, on occasion, "both penitent and confessor are borne together to the grave."

The high death rate in the clergy reflected parish priests ministering to the sick. Many enclosed orders of friars and nuns were wiped out when a member of the community fell ill and transmitted the disease within the group. Pneumonic plague seems to have been common in Ireland. Typically, twenty to thirty percent of the population of Cork died. It was a significant factor in the shrinkage of English-controlled land to the area of the Pale around Dublin.

Plague Doctors

Venice, the major European port of entrance for the exotic silks and spices coming into the continent via the silk route, was subject to plague on a regular basis. The Doge and city council were among the first to appoint three state-paid doctors, who undertook not to flee the city when plague struck. John Julius Norwich suggests that this was the first National Health Service. The policy was taken up in many other city states but, plague doctors were basically only hired when an epidemic struck. Pope Clement VI hired extra plague doctors when the Black Death came to Avignon.

Plague doctors were often poorly qualified, or even lacked any medical training. They were called community plague doctors, to distinguish them from established general practitioners and were supposed to confine their practices to treating plague victims and none other. They were well paid and wore protective clothing. As time progressed, their attire became formalised.

They carried a stick, which had two uses. Firstly, it enabled them to examine victims by lifting up the garments without physically touching the patients. Secondly, as many victims believed plague was a punishment imposed on them for sin, they often requested the doctor to beat them with the stick to expiate their guilt.

Plague doctors were required to keep records of deaths, advise on wills and in some instances, perform autopsies. In truth, standard medical treatment at the time was not only useless but may have even hastened death. As it was generally accepted by the medical profession that the disease was spread by humors, one of the suggested preventative measures was to inhale competing foul odours, such as existed in latrines.

A multiplicity of herbal protective potions were used. One of these was the "form of vinegar" – a mix of vinegar, herbs, spices and garlic. Folklore had it that such a mixture was used by thieves who stole possessions and travelling jewellery from plague victims. By using the mixture, they were themselves protected from catching the disease.

Doctors applied leeches or frogs to the buboes and, even resorted to placing sacrificed young pigeons, split open, to the lesions. Most doctors advised blood-letting, which paradoxically hastened death.

Nostradamus was an exception. He advised fresh air, rose hip juice, the removal of dead bodies but did not recommend bleeding.

An Italian doctor recommended drinking a full glass of good red wine before dinner. The wine to be neither too dry or too sweet!

Consecrated burial grounds were overwhelmed and burial often took place in pits. It was difficult to get persons to take dead bodies for burial. In Florence, well paid Beccamorti (vultures) carried the bodies to the grave.

An Irish doctor, Niall Ó Glacáin, became famous for his care of plague patients in later years. He survived multiple exposures and ended his career a professor in Bologna.

Summary

The Black Death was the most disastrous epidemic in Europe to date. Almost certainly caused by variants of the bacillum, *Yersinia pestis*, it killed an estimated 100 million people worldwide. A quarter of Europe's population died and, it took 150 years for this to recover. At the time, it was perceived as a pestilence sent by God to punish evil. Alternative explanations included planetary conjunction of Saturn, Jupiter and Mars. Plague made no distinction between prince or pauper but, moneyed classes had more mobility and were sometimes able to outrun the disease.

Further Reading

History of the Black Death in Ireland by M.A. Kelly (Tempus. 2004)

The Greatest Benefit to Mankind by R. Porter (Harper Collins. 1997)

Shakespeare's Restless World by N. MacGregor (Penguin. 2013)

The Plantagenets by D. Jones (William Collins. 2013)

The Popes by John Julius Norwich (Vintage. 2011)

"Climate-driven introduction of the Black Death and successive plague reintroductions into Europe" by BV Schmid et al in *Proceedings of the National Academy of Science of the USA* (10 March 2015)

Pellagra

Asturian Leprosy

Deficiency diseases are now rare in Ireland. Scurvy is seen from time to time, typically in bachelor farmers existing on bread, jam and tea. Severe dieting can lead to mineral and vitamin deficiency, such as Niacin (B3), as can alcoholism. When diet was the mainstay of duodenal ulcer, Xeropthalmia due to Vitamin A deficiency occurred. My late father suffered from this as a medical student in the 1930s, probably due to over-strict adherence to the Bertram Welton Sippy diet.

It took the medical profession an uncommonly long time to accept that pellagra was a deficiency disease. That it might be diet related was also resisted by the political establishment as an inconvenient truth.

Pellagra was a scourge in rural Italy, especially in the northeast, where it reached epidemic proportions, affecting as many as 150,000 known victims in the late 19th century.

Pellagra was documented in 1902 in the USA. It reached epidemic proportions in the southern states in the early 20th century, affecting three million and causing 100,000 deaths. Unfortunate sufferers were treated with remedies such as arsenic, Salvarsan, calcium sulphide, strychnine, quinine autoserotherapy, partial appendectomy and electro-convulsive therapy!

Clinically, pellagra manifests as the three D's: dermatitis, diarrhoea and dementia. Sadly, for too long, there was a fourth D – namely, death.

Asturian Leprosy

This was first described by Gaspar Casals in 1735 in the province of Asturias in northern Spain. While he called it "mal de rosa", after the characteristic sun-sensitive, red rash on the back of the hands and feet, it became colloquially known as "Asturian leprosy". A rash on the neck delimited by clothing is considered a pathognomonic feature now called "Casal's necklace".

An Italian physician, Francesco Frapoli, coined the term, pellagra, in 1771 from the Bergamo-dialect Italian, *pelle* (skin) and *agra* (rough). Sufferers were collectively known as Pelligrosi. Pellagraphobia often led to them being shunned as perceived lepers. Such stigmatisation undoubtedly led to gross underestimation of sufferers in a community.

It is a widespread misconception that leprosy, as referred to in the Bible, was an infectious disease. It is clear that the so-called characteristic skin features looked for by the priests included vitiligo and pellagra. Leprosy was considered a manifestation of sin. This was the reason for lepers to live apart. It was accepted that lepers could recover. A priest had to examine those who recovered before they were readmitted to the community.

When the Conquistadors introduced New World crops, such as maize, tomatoes, beans and potatoes to Europe at the end of the 16th Century, it seemed very advantageous. Unfortunately, especially in Italy, it had tragic consequences. Maize had many advantages to the farmer, farm owners and the state. Its yield was phenomenal compared to wheat and if the wheat crop failed, maize could still be planted. Cheap and plentiful, it became the staple of polenta, the primary foodstuff of the poor, especially in winter and spring.

In the 1760s, Jacopo Odoardi in the Veneto described the dermatitis and oral manifestations of pellagra. These were followed by languor and ultimately madness. He called it "Italic scurvy". Most doctors then concluded that a maize diet was in some way responsible. It was accepted that it was not hereditary or infectious and affected women more commonly than men.

Two Italian physicians duelled as to its fundamental cause in the late 19th Century. Clodomiro Bonfiglia was Director of an insane asylum in Ferrara. He concluded that pellagra was the result of hunger and reliance on a diet of maize polenta for six months of the year. Cesar Lombroso, Director of an insane ward in Pavia insisted it was the poor quality of some maize that was responsible. He claimed to have isolated the specific toxin responsible from mouldy maize. Lombroso was Italy's most famous doctor internationally, at the time, and it was his theory that became accepted officially. Bonfiglia's belief that it was a social problem was conveniently sidelined.

It took 50 years before those championing the toxic cause yielded to deficiency theorists. Tryptophan acts as a precursor of niacin, with approximately one sixtieth the activity of the vitamin. In assessing foodstuff, the "niacin equivalent" is a better index of availability of the vitamin than total niacin content.

The American epidemic, which started at the beginning of the 20th century, was initially blamed on Italian immigrants. Pellagraphobia, akin to when AIDS was first recognised, was widespread. Many hospitals refused admission to sufferers and those who did imposed strict isolation. By 1912, 25,000 cases had been diagnosed in the southern states, with a 40% mortality.

In 1914, Joseph Goldberger was appointed head of the US Public Health Service pellagra investigation. Within three months, he had concluded that it was a diet related rather than an infectious disease. He observed that pellagra in mental institutions was confined to the patients and never affected doctors, nurses or attendants. He noted it was a rural disease associated with a monotonous "3M" diet comprising meat (fat back), corn meal and molasses. He advised increased intake of milk, eggs and fresh meat.

Twelve convicts were promised a pardon for participating in a study. All were previously healthy white prisoners. After six months on the "3M" diet, six of the eleven remaining in the study had developed pellagra. To prove it was not transmissible, he exposed 16 volunteers (including his wife) to blood, urine, faeces and skin scrapings of sufferers. None developed pellagra. He postulated that it was due to dietary deficiency in the poor. He showed that dried yeast was an effective cure. He postulated the existence of a pellagra preventive factor (P-P factor) and opined that this factor would turn out to be one of the water-soluble B vitamins.

He died in 1929 and in 1937, Conrad A. Elvehjem isolated nicotinic acid (niacin), the elusive P-P factor.

Nixtamalisation
How was it that a staple of the Mesoamerican diet for centuries was toxic when introduced as a crop elsewhere? The answer lay in the way in which it was prepared. In Mesoamerica, maize was typically soaked and cooked in lime water, an alkaline solution, a process known as nixtamalisation. This process rendered the grain more easily ground, increased its flavour and reduced mycotoxins. When introduced to Europe nixtamalisation was not performed, due to the availability of mechanical milling machines. Maize thus prepared in Europe was rendered a much less nutritional food by preventing bound niacin becoming free niacin, available for absorption.

Madness and Pellagra
The third clinical stage of pellagra is dementia. Delirium better describes it. Depression, disorientation and confusion can progress to mania and violent behaviour. Paranoid hallucinations can develop with cog wheel rigidity, grasping and sucking reflexes. Niacin replacement is dramatically effective in reversing these signs and symptoms.

A tragic example of this delirium is the celebrated case of Mattio Lovat. A shoemaker by trade in the Dolomites, he developed "leprous" eruptions on his face and hands. In July 1802, he was seized by religious mania and castrated himself. Surviving this, he moved to Venice, where he became obsessed with the idea of crucifying himself. In 1805, he nailed his feet and one hand to a cross and threw himself out of a window.

Cesar Ruggieri, a Venetian surgeon, was among passers-by who rescued him. Ruggieri treated his wounds and had him transferred to hospital. Lovat died six months later in the lunatic asylum on San Servolo, an island in the Venetian lagoon. Ruggieri's report of the case identified pellagra as the cause of Lovat's madness. It is one of the first known descriptions of madness in pellagra and was described as evidence of "religious mania".

It is probable that some of the 50,000 victims executed as witches between 1500 and 1700 were suffering from pellagra.

Female Preponderance

All studies of pellagra worldwide show a preponderance of females among the adults affected. In rural Italy, where food was limited, a woman typically fed the man first, then the children, often leaving herself the smallest portion. Women not only ate less calories but worked as hard or harder than men.

We know now that women require more niacin than men for physiological and hormonal reasons. The female preponderance of pelligrosi persisted in the third stage of the disease, as reflected in mental asylum admissions. Over 60% of pellagra induced mental disease in Italy as a whole was in women. That percentage was even higher in the Veneto, where maize growing was first established and the crop hailed as "Venetian glory".

Pellagra almost certainly reduced sex drive. Amenorrhoea occurred in women and male testes were said to atrophy with loss of pubic hair. Inadequate records prevent us from stating with scientific certainty that fertility was reduced in sufferers.

Pellagra Today

Pellagra still exists in Africa (especially in Zimbabwe and Angola), India, Nepal and North Korea. It was common in the Soviet Gulags. Refugees comprise a high-risk population. In Ireland, it can result from severe dieting, malabsorption, as in Crohn's disease and alcoholism.

It can be caused by long-term use of Isoniazid, as the drug replaces nicotinamide in the coenzyme NAD (nicotinamide adenine dinucleotide).

It can occur in pheochromocytoma where tryptophan is diverted to form 5 hydroxytryptamine and carcinoid tumours, where tryptophan is used up to produce serotonin.

Hartnup's disease is an autosomal recessive disorder, where tryptophan absorption fails due to a transport defect in the intestinal lining and the proximal convoluted tubules in the kidney, causing light sensitivity and pellagrinous skin lesions.

Further Reading

"Peasants and Pellagra in 19th Century Italy" by David Gentilcore in *History Today* (2014), 64.9:48-54

"Pellagra in the United States: A Historical Perspective" by Kumarvel Rajakumar in *Southern Medical Journal* (2000), 93.3:272-277

Malaria

Controversy and Transmission

mal'aria: (Italian) = *bad air*

Malaria in Ireland is currently non-endemic. This has not always been the case. Before 1844, indigenous malaria was almost unknown in Cork but from the mid-1850s, it became endemic. This coincided with the Crimean War (1854-1858). Regiments sailed from Cork to the Crimea and returning veterans were often heavily infected with malaria.

The anopheline mosquito needs a minimum temperature of 60° Fahrenheit for two weeks to complete its cycle. The summers of 1856 and 1857 were remarkably hot in Cork and extended into the autumn. Coincidentally, minor epidemics were recorded in England in 1848 and the early 1850s. In the *Transactions* of the Cork Medical Society, Dr Carey, Royal Artillery Military Barracks, Ballincollig Co Cork recorded 663 cases of malaria in the period 1854-1860.

In 1857-1858, it reached epidemic proportions. In reply to a survey by the society, 14 members recorded a total of 917 cases seen by them. This certainly represents a small proportion of the total cases in the epidemic. Dr Jackson Cummins reported seeing 113 cases in his practice. He speculated that the building of the marina in Blackrock to contain the river Lee, which created a large inland swamp, may have provided an ideal breeding ground for mosquitoes.

Details of the epidemic were presented to the society in an historic paper by Major Michael Whelton RAMC (my uncle) in 1934. Between 1863 and 1878, the epidemic subsided. In an era of global warming, the possibility that mosquitoes capable of transmitting malaria could again breed in Ireland cannot be excluded.

Cinchona: Jesuit's Bark

Malaria is no respecter of rank or privilege. Pope Urban VIII (1623-1644) was a driving force in the quest for a cure. His predecessor, Sixtus, had died of the disease and Urban was struck down by it immediately after his election as Pope. No less than eight of the Cardinals in the Conclave that elected him died of the disease.

A Jesuit apothecary, Augustino Salumbrino, in Peru had observed that the Querca Indians used the bark of the Cinchona tree to treat chills. He thought it might have a role in non-specific fever and sent some samples to Rome. Trials showed that the bark not only worked in controlling chills but also cured the disease. We now know that it was the quinine it contained that was curative. Cardinal Lugo funded provision of the drug to the poor. It became variously known as "de Lugo's Powder", "Cardinals Powder" and later, almost exclusively, as "Jesuits Bark". When Oliver Cromwell lay dying of malaria at the age of 54 years, he steadfastly refused to take a "Popish" cure.

Ronald Ross

"A tall man with a very red face. A peppery manner and a stiff moustache – the conventional embodiment of the retired officer from India of his generation."
– Harley Williams

Ross was a man of his times who firmly believed in the British Empire and what it stood for. He viewed malaria as "a gigantic ally of barbarism", preventing safe settlement of "the pioneers of civilisation."

He was born in Almira, North West Provinces of India in 1857, son of a British Army General. He was schooled in England, excelling in mathematics, poetry and music. He favoured a career as a writer but, his father enrolled him in St Bartholomew's Medical School in London. His undergraduate career was less than distinguished and he passed his Final medical examination (MB BS) on the second attempt. He joined the Medical Service of the British Army in India. Importantly, he took leave to take a diploma course in Bacteriology.

Alphonse Lavaran (1845-1922), a French army doctor, discovered protozoan parasites in the blood smear of a patient who had recently died of malaria. Described as "Lavaran's Organism", it was later renamed, Plasmodium. It was the first time a protozoan organism had been identified as a cause of human disease. Ross was frustrated in his attempts to identify this organism. Patrick Manson the "father of Tropical Medicine" discovered the cause and mode of transmission of Elephantiasis, a filarial disease. He introduced the concept of insect vector transmission of disease, differing from the accepted European concept of water or airborne disease. Not only did he show Ross the staining techniques to identify Lavaran's organism but far more importantly, speculated that malaria might be transmitted by mosquitoes.

Manson further suggested that India might be the ideal place to research its transmission, due to the abundance of malaria in the subcontinent. Manson added a word of caution, telling Ross that, in the event of him proving the mode of transmission, "the Frenchies and the Italians will pooh-pooh it and claim it as their own."

Immediately on his return to India, Ross set about examining blood smears from sufferers and dissecting mosquitoes. In May 1895, he identified the early stages of a malaria parasite in a mosquito stomach. Two years of frustrating failure followed.

In June 1897, he managed to culture 20 adult dapple-winged mosquitoes from larvae. He attempted to infect the mosquitoes by allowing them to bite an Indian male patient with malaria. He painstakingly dissected the mosquitoes. The first 18 yielded nothing. In the stomachs of the last two insects he found "peculiar pigmented cells", which clearly differed from mosquito stomach cells. He sent the slides to Manson for independent assessment. He wrote up his findings and submitted the paper to the *British Medical Journal*, where it was duly published.

His research was regularly disrupted by changes of army posting, often to areas with little indigenous malaria. With reluctance, he followed Manson's advice to study bird malaria. It was using this model, in infected larks, that he showed mosquitoes were the vectors of bird malaria and that the organisms were stored in the salivary glands being transmitted when the mosquito bit to feed. He successfully transmitted malaria parasites to healthy birds. He was posted away from Calcutta to study kala-azar (black fever), leaving him unable to confirm his avian findings in humans.

Giovanni Battista Grassi

Grassi was an Italian physician and zoologist. He qualified in Medicine in 1878. He began his studies of malaria in 1883. He discovered the malaria parasite of birds, Plasmodium praecox, in 1891 and successfully inoculated malaria parasites from one bird to another. He was convinced malaria only occurred where there were mosquitoes but accepted the likelihood that not all mosquitoes transmitted the disease. He also discovered the parasite, Plasmodium vivax. He showed that it was the female Anopheles mosquito that was the vector. He described malaria developing in a healthy volunteer after being bitten by Anopheles mosquitoes and later, that this species became infected on biting a diseased person. He showed that the different clinical courses taken in human malaria were due to the specific infecting organism. Benign tertian was caused by Plasmodium vivax, malignant tertian by Plasmodium falciparum and quartan by Plasmodium malaria.

In 1898, he succeeded in transmitting malaria to uninfected subjects by mosquito bite. He thus proved the transmission theory of Ross' avian studies applied to humans.

Nobel Prize

The Nobel Prize Committee in Medicine or Physiology in 1902 initially favoured awarding the prize jointly to Ross and Grassi. Unfortunately, Ross launched a bitter attack on Grassi, claiming primacy in the discovery of the mode of malaria transmission. Moreover, he called Grassi "a fraud and a pirate."

The mild-mannered Grassi engaged in heated exchanges with the militant Ross. Another nominee for the prize that year was Robert Koch, who was widely respected and considered the founder of modern Bacteriology. Koch approached the committee to act as a "neutral" arbitrator, even though Grassi had pointed out flaws in Koch's research into malaria in 1898.

Reportedly, Koch came down heavily in favour of awarding the prize solely to Ross but, it was Grassi who demonstrated that it was the female Anopheles mosquito that was responsible for human transmission. (Ross was not a zoologist and got no further than identifying it as a "grey dappled mosquito"). Grassi also worked out the life cycle of Plasmodium falciparum, resolved the conundrum of the different clinical courses of malaria and proved that human malaria was transmitted by mosquito bite. By any standards, he deserved to share the prize.

Epilogue

The bitterness and rancour surrounding the flawed decision lasted for decades. Robert Koch's intervention reflects no credit on him. Koch was finally awarded the prize himself in 1905. In these days of peer review, Ross' seminal paper with its small numbers and lack of controls would stand little chance of being accepted for publication. We must be grateful to the then editor of the *British Medical Journal* of the day, for publishing it.

One can only speculate, had Jesuit's bark been known by a name without religious connotations, would Oliver Cromwell have taken it and survived malaria? Had he done so, the Protectorate would have been prolonged and the restoration of King Charles II may never have occurred. In the event, Cromwell's son, Richard – or "Queen Dick" as he became derisively known – lacked his father's authority and renounced power after nine months.

Further Reading

Some Chapters of Cork Medical History by N. Marshall Cummins (Cork University Press. 1957)

Masters of Medicine by Harley Williams (Pan Books, London. 1954)

Herod the Great

Reviled for the Wrong Reasons?

Herod's final illness was probably chronic renal failure with associated scrotal myiasis. It is likely that he suffered from Schistosomiasis, resulting from infection with *Schistosoma mansoni*. Josephus records that Herod developed "a putrefaction of his privy parts that produced worms."

It has been speculated that this was the rare condition, Fournier gangrene. A more likely diagnosis is myiasis or fly infestation of oedematous genitalia, with resultant maggot growth.

Paranoid and with good reason, Herod was ruthless and had one wife and three sons executed. Paradoxically then, the event recorded by Matthew, the Massacre of the Innocents, by which he is still reviled by Christians, is historically uncertain.

"Then Herod, when he saw that he was mocked by the wise men, was exceeding wroth, and sent forth, and slew all the children that were in Bethlehem, and in all the coasts thereof, from two years and under, according to the time which he had diligently inquired of the wise men".
– Matthew 2:16

The Massacre of the Innocents is only recorded in passing in the Gospel of Matthew. The event has been a favourite one, particularly with Christian tradition painters, including Peter Paul Rubens. It symbolised the cruelty and wickedness of that King. Traditionally, the numbers killed were believed to be in the thousands. While he carried out many criminal acts in the 40 years that he ruled the Roman client state of Judea, it is likely that the event he is most remembered for never occurred or, at worst, has been grossly exaggerated.

Herod the Great was father of Herod Antipas – the Herod of the Gospels. Jesus was born in Bethlehem in the year 5 or 6 BC. Joseph was probably living with his family at the time. Luke, confused by the fact that the Holy Family had lived in Nazareth for such a long period, had to invent a reason for siting them in Bethlehem for the birth, hence the story of the census.

In Bethlehem, many houses were built in front of caves, where domestic animals were sheltered in bad weather. Joseph probably moved Mary out of the hurly burly of the living quarters into the quieter, warm cave area for the birth hence, the perception of Jesus being laid in a manger.

Herod's supposed decree was issued within a year of Jesus' birth. A number of contradictions become evident when the story is examined. Firstly, Herod had a widespread network of spies and appears to have directed the Wise Men to Bethlehem. If he really wanted to eliminate this child Messiah, as a perceived threat to his rule, he could easily have done so without relying on information from three men from the East, whom he hardly knew.

Next, Bethlehem was a small village with a population in the region of 300 and not exceeding 1000 in its environs. The killing was to be confined to male children two years and under – i.e. children who had not entered their second year. The numbers could not have been more than 10 to 20 infants. If the incident took place, why is it not mentioned in the other Synoptic Gospels of Mark and Luke? The Roman historian, Josephus, likewise does not reference it though, the killing of a few infants in a remote village might not have appeared to be historically significant.

Joseph, warned in a dream by an angel about the imminent infanticide, left Bethlehem for Egypt. The time spent in Egypt is widely commemorated by the Coptic Church there. According to Matthew, they remained there until Herod died.

"And was there until the death of Herod." – **Matthew 2:15**

On their return from Egypt, the family moved to Nazareth because of the continuing insecurity under the Herodian dynasty. Another factor in their relocation could have been Joseph's feeling of guilt at not having warned others of the danger while saving his own son.

Herod was himself half-Jewish. Born in 73BC, his father, Antipater, was chief minister to King Hyrcanus II of the Maccabee dynasty. Julius Caesar appointed Antipater governor of Judea in 41 BC and in turn, Antipater appointed his son, Herod, Governor of Galilee. After a bitter civil war, the Roman Senate voted to make Herod "King of the Jews".

He was a figure of hatred to many Jews, especially the powerful Pharisee grouping. He married ten times and had 14 children. Almost certainly, there were more children as females were not always recorded. He divorced his first wife, Doris, in favour of Mariamne, daughter of Hyrcanus, the former King. He later executed Hyrcanus.

His achievements were substantial. He built the port city of Caesarea, the largest man-made harbour in the Mediterranean, considered by many to be a wonder of the world. He rebuilt the second temple in Jerusalem, of which, the last supporting wall, The Wailing Wall, still stands. He built aqueducts amphitheatres and fortresses (including Masada).

He established a network of spies and was ruthless in eliminating real or perceived enemies. He had his wife's brother, who was high priest, murdered by drowning and killed close on 50 of the powerful Sanhedrin. Even though Mariamne was his favourite wife, he ultimately had her executed on dubious grounds of adultery and later killed his two sons by her. Augustus in Rome was said to have remarked that he would rather be Herod's pig than his son, as the Jews don't eat pigs!

Josephus relates Herod's symptoms and signs in his final illness as intolerable itching, abdominal pain, peripheral oedema and "gangrene of his privy parts that produced worms."

Fly infestation, myiasis of his oedematous scrotum with subsequent development of maggots seems the likely explanation of this. Other suggestions are that he had the rare condition, Fournier gangrene. Polyarteritis nodosa has been proposed as the cause of his nephropathy. It is likely he suffered from Schistosomiasis, possibly with portal hypertension though, this would not explain the intolerable itch referred to by Josephus. He could not have suffered from syphilis, as that disease had not yet been introduced from the Americas.

He may have suffered from depression and had good reason to be paranoid. At the time that the Wise Men visited him, his brother, Pheroras, was plotting to poison him. Pheroras' wife, Jochebed, also announced that her soon-to-be-born son was the promised Messiah! Given that he was terminally ill and a follower of the Jewish faith, perhaps he genuinely wished for the arrival of a Messiah to follow him and reclaim the Kingdom for the Jews from the Romans. His instruction to the Wise Men was "Bring me word that I also may come and worship him."

Maybe his motives have been misconstrued. He was in such pain and distress towards the end of his life that he attempted suicide with a fruit knife. Increasingly paranoid, he had his son (by Doris, his first wife), Antipater, executed days before he died. He also ordered a gathering together of the most accomplished men in the Kingdom, to have them executed the day he himself died. Fortunately for them, his son and daughter countermanded the order and they were spared.

Summary

Herod the Great was a complex man. Appointed by Rome as King of the Jews, he ruled the client state of Judea. He was energetic and resourceful. He built Caesarea Maritima, the biggest man-made port in the Mediterranean. Possibly suffering long-term depression and definitely paranoid, he executed one wife and three sons in his immediate family. Others executed included his brother-in-law, the High Priest and many members of the Sanhedrin. Herod observed mosaic dietary laws scrupulously leading Caesar Augustus to famously remark, "I would rather be Herod's pig than his son."

It is paradoxical then that he is most reviled for a crime – the Massacre of the Innocents – which, in all probability, never took place.

Further Reading

Monsters by Simon Sebag Montefiore (Quercus, London. 2009)

The Holy Land by J. Murphy-O'Connor (Oxford University Press. 1980)

Magna Carta
Was King John all Bad?

In West Cork, wild broom adds its splash of yellow every Spring to that of the ever-flowering gorse. Geoffrey IV wore a sprig of yellow broom in his cap. The Latin name, *planta genista*, led to the dynasty he founded becoming known as the Plantagenets.

The Cork arms shows two castles with a sailing boat between. Queen's Castle stood to the north and King's Castle to the south. As Lord of Ireland, Prince John granted the charter to build King's Castle and fortify the city. His place in history is, however, sealed by an event which occurred more than 800 years ago, in June 1215.

In a meadow in Runnymede on the Thames, the now King John signed a peace treaty with his barons – the Magna Carta. As a peace treaty, it failed almost immediately. Indeed, both sides had reservations about its contents though John had most to lose. Having had his previous excommunication expunged, John looked to the Pope for support. Innocent III issued a papal bull stating, "we utterly reject and condemn this settlement and under threat of excommunication, we order that the King should not dare to observe it – we declare it null and void of all validity forever."

I grew up with tales of Robin Hood, the Sheriff of Nottingham and bad King John but does he deserve his evil reputation? On balance, he does, even by standards of the time. His older brother, Richard the Lionheart, initially named his nephew, Arthur of Brittany, as his heir in the event of his death in the Third Crusade. On his deathbed, his mother, Eleanor of Aquitaine, persuaded him to name John – who had not "taken the cross" and thus exempted himself from joining the Crusade – as heir. This was despite the fact that John had intrigued against Richard, trying to supplant him as king while he was on crusade, going as far as to pay homage to the French King.

John even tried to bribe the German Emperor to keep his brother prisoner rather than release him on payment of a ransom. When Richard was freed, John threw himself at his feet in Paris and begged forgiveness.

As King, John rarely showed prowess on the battlefield. An exception was when he rescued his mother from capture. With Hugh de Lusignon, whose young wife John had abducted, Arthur attempted to take his grandmother hostage. John force marched his men 80 miles and foiled the attempt. Arthur and de Lusignon were captured. Despite assurances to the contrary, Arthur was incarcerated in brutal conditions. A childless John clearly still feared Arthur's claim to the throne. He instructed the gaoler to blind and castrate the 16-year-old. The gaoler, Hubert de Burg, recoiled from the order but fearing the King's wrath, put out a story that Arthur had died of natural causes.

Discovering the truth, John had the prisoner moved to a dungeon in Rouen Castle. John entered the cell in a drunken rage and killed his nephew, tied a stone to the body and threw it in the Seine. This, ultimately, led to the invasion of England by the French under Prince Louis, who was welcomed by the Barons despite a threat of excommunication from the Papal Legate. John desperately hung on to the throne but, after a disastrous miscalculation of the tides in the Wash, where he lost most of his baggage train, he developed dysentery and died.

John was a cruel and devious man but not much worse than his brother and father. He did not inspire confidence. He was also vindictive, indecisive, arrogant, paranoid and untrustworthy. His weak personality, his pursuit of vendettas and the loss of almost all Plantagenet land in France sets him apart. He had the bad luck to rule in a time of waning absolute power. Little could he have imagined that the Magna Carta would become such a defining and historic document. Reissued after 10 years, it was nailed to church doors and displayed in town squares all over England.

It is paradoxical that a failed peace treaty, signed more than 800 years ago, has come to define the duty of those who govern to rule within the law.

King Richard III

Tyrant or Not?

"And seem a saint when most I play the devil"
– Richard III, Act 1, Scene 3

The remains of Richard III of England were exhumed from the site of the former Greyfriars Church, Leicester in September 2012. Positive identification was achieved by skeletal analysis and DNA testing. The spine revealed a right-sided scoliosis. Maternal line DNA testing on two 14th cousins of his sister, Anne of York, confirmed the remains were those of Richard III. Paternal line genetic information did not match living relatives. This is ascribed to infidelity or cuckolding. The rate of false paternity is estimated at one or two percent per generation. Despite this, the overwhelming evidence is that the remains are those of the last English King to be killed in battle.

Richard reigned from 1483 to 1485. A Yorkist, he was defeated and killed by the Lancastrian, Henry Tudor at the Battle of Bosworth Field. Analysis of his skeletal remains have helped to make a factual assessment of his physical disabilities. They have also given a good indication of the injuries which caused his death. It suited his Tudor enemies to exaggerate his physical deformity. Inevitably, our perceptions of his personality and tyranny are coloured by Shakespeare's eponymous play.

Physical Deformity

In the 15th century, physical deformity was seen as a manifestation of evil. Contemporary accounts describe Richard as an ugly child with protruding teeth and excess body hair.

Shakespeare depicts him as a hunchback with a withered arm who walked with a limp.

Appleby et al. (2014), in a detailed analysis of the remains, found that he was of short build with a spiral, right-sided scoliosis of the thoracic spine. These findings fit with contemporary accounts, which describe him as small of stature, light build and having unequal shoulders – the right higher than the left. Portraits confirm the higher right shoulder. The scoliosis was well compensated. He was not a hunchback. Likewise, analysis of the skeleton showed symmetrical, well-formed leg bones incompatible with a significant limp. The scoliosis appears to be of idiopathic adolescent onset, probably starting after the age of ten years.

Perimortem Trauma

Appleby et al. (2015) have studied the remains forensically and made an analysis of perimortem trauma. They have attempted to identify which injuries could have been fatal and, in so far as possible, how they were inflicted. Unfortunately, the order in which the injuries were inflicted cannot be established.

They identify three which could have been fatal. Richard would have been wearing armour at the time of his death but, his helmet must have been lost or removed. No defensive wounds were identified on his arms or hands, suggesting that, apart from his helmet, he was fully armed when killed. All the skeletal injuries identified were recent and none were healed.

There were nine perimortem injuries to the skull and two to the postcranial skeleton. There were three major skull fractures. One, on the sagittal suture, is likely to have been caused by a blow delivered from above a prone victim by a roundel dagger. This would not have been immediately fatal. A second was on the inferior aspect of the skull, on the right side of the occipital bone. This is consistent with a blow from a large, bladed weapon, either a sword, halberd or bill. The third was adjacent to the foramen magnum on the left, on the inferior surface of the occipital bone. This injury is also consistent with a blow from a sword tip or the spike of a bill or halberd. Either of these two injuries, if inflicted in life, could have been fatal. Both are consistent with being inflicted on a prone body or, with the victim kneeling with the head pointing downwards.

A further fracture was present in the right maxilla, consistent with a penetrating injury to the right cheek inflicted by a dagger. On its own, this would have been non-fatal. Preservation of the face from more severe structural damage may relate to the need of Henry Tudor to display the dead body, to prevent pretenders claiming the throne in Richard's name.

The other potentially fatal injury was identified in the pelvis. Here, there was evidence of a fine-bladed instrument entering the right buttock and traversing the pelvic cavity. Richard's body armour and war saddle should have protected him from such a wound during battle. It seems likely that this was inflicted after he was stripped of his armour and, his dead body slung over a horse.

On the balance of probability then, the blows to the occipital region of the skull are likely to have been the fatal ones.

Tyrant or Not?

When his father, Richard, 3rd Duke of York, was killed in battle, Richard's eldest brother was proclaimed King Edward IV. Initially, Richard appeared loyal to Edward and, was rewarded with the title, Duke of Gloucester, much land and a military command in the north of England. When the Lancastrian, Henry I, was briefly restored, he went into exile with his brother and in turn, helped him to regain the crown.

Another older brother, the Duke of Clarence, was impeached for treason in 1478 and drowned in a butt of malmsey wine in the Tower of London. Richard conspired with Edward in the death of this brother.

On Edward's unexpected death in April 1483, Richard assumed the role of guardian to Edward's 12-year-old heir. The Royal Council discussed Edward V's coronation on 10 June. The following day, Richard claimed to have uncovered a plot by Edwards widow, Elizabeth and her associates to seize power. William, Lord Hastings, chamberlain and friend of Edward IV was arrested and summarily executed in the Tower of London for "conspiracy".

Queen Elizabeth had taken sanctuary in Westminster but, was tricked into releasing the other prince, nine-year-old Richard, Duke of York, into his uncle's custody, on the basis that he was needed to attend the coronation of his brother as Edward V. He placed both princes in the Tower, supposedly for their safe keeping. He then announced the postponement of the coronation until November. It was anticipated that a protectorate would be set up, in view of the youth of the heir.

By now, Richard was undoubtedly planning a coup d'état. His claim to the throne was publicised in a sermon by Dr Ralph Shaw in June. Two perceived rivals, Rivers (the Queen's brother) and Grey were executed without trial that month. He then claimed his brother, Edward IV, was illegitimate but, later modified this to a claim that Edward's marriage to Elizabeth Woodruff was null and void, as Edward had supposedly contracted to marry another. This scenario now cast the princes in the Tower as bastards. The princes were last seen playing in the Tower that summer after which, they inexplicably "disappeared". It was not until 1674 that two children's skeletons, now widely believed to be those of the princes, were found under a staircase in the Tower.

Richard was crowned in June 1483. In the autumn, there was a poorly coordinated rebellion that was easily put down. Richard used this as an excuse to execute Stafford, Duke of Buckingham and many of the rebels who were, in the main, Yorkists who had been loyal to his brother, Edward IV. He confiscated their estates and distributed them among his supporters.

He had his own personal tragedies: his son dying in 1484 and his wife in 1485.

Over his reign, his violence and disregard of the law alienated and frightened many erstwhile Yorkist supporters. This led to his undoing at the Battle of Bosworth Field. The northern establishment deserted him, Northumberland stood apart and the Stanleys actively supported Henry Tudor. He fought valiantly, almost reaching Henry before being cut down. He was 32 years old.

Conclusion

Remains discovered in a car park on the former site of a church in Leicester are proven to be those of Richard III. Forensic analysis of his skeleton confirms his physical deformities were exaggerated by his Tudor rivals and the myth perpetuated by Shakespeare. He did have a scoliosis but, was not a hunchback and did not have a pronounced limp. Analysis of the skeleton has revealed 11 perimortem injuries. Injuries not affecting the skeleton cannot be ruled out.

Near contemporary battle accounts suggest he abandoned his bogged down horse continuing to fight on foot. The skull wounds indicate he had lost his helmet or, had it removed. As there was no skeletal evidence of defensive wounds on his arms, it seems probable that he was still in armour other than the helmet.

While the sequence in which he received his injuries cannot be established, it is probable that the fatal blows were those to the inferior cranium. These are consistent with blows delivered by the top spike of a bill, halberd or sword tip.

He was the last Plantagenet king. Paradoxically, Henry Tudor, who succeeded him, had a much weaker claim to the throne. Henry married Elizabeth, sister of the princes in the tower. The Tudor rose combines the white of York and the red of Lancaster, symbolising the end of the War of the Roses.

Further Reading

"A Hog Under the Law" by S. Cooper and A. Cooper in *History Today* (2013), vol 63 issue 11:35-40

"The scoliosis of Richard III, the last Plantagenet King of England" by Jo Appleby, Piers D. Mitchell, Claire Robinson et al in *Lancet* (2014), 383:2014

"Richard III: skeletal evidence of perimortem trauma" by Heather E. Bonney in *Lancet* (2015), 210

"Perimortem trauma in King Richard III: a skeletal analysis" by Jo Appleby, Guy N. Rutty, Sarah V. Hainsworth et al in *Lancet* (2015) 385: 253-259

Caravaggio: Knight of Malta
and Sufferer from Chronic Lead Poisoning

Michelangelo Merisi (Caravaggio) had a turbulent career. He became one of Italy's foremost and sought-after painters in his short lifetime. Born a commoner, he became obsessed with the possibility of becoming a Knight of Malta. Apart from the prestige of a knighthood, he desperately needed all the support he could muster to receive a papal pardon for a death sentence imposed on him for murder. Against all the odds, he became a Knight of Malta but only retained the title for four-and-a-half months. A papal pardon was eventually obtained but Caravaggio died on his return journey from Naples to Rome. Recent evaluation of his remains suggest that he suffered chronic lead poisoning and this, maybe, explained some of his aggressive behaviour and mood swings.

Michelangelo Merisi was born in Lombardy in 1571. He came to be called Caravaggio after the town east of Milan, in which was the family home. His early life was spent in Milan but, his family moved back to Caravaggio, in a vain effort to avoid the plague, when he was six years old. His father died of the plague soon after their arrival in the home town.

Michelangelo moved back to Milan and, at age 13, took up an apprenticeship contract with the painter Peterzano. At the end of the apprenticeship, he returned to Caravaggio, where his mother died the following year.

Caravaggio was then 18 and two years later, he realised his inheritance and left for Rome, never to return to his family town. By now he was known as a violent man in violent times and was an accomplished swordsman. His arrival in Rome coincided with urban renewal under Pope Sixtus V. Having spent his inheritance rapidly, he was forced to paint pictures for sale, a practice forbidden by the Artists Guild.

A Sicilian painter, Mario Menetti, befriended him and this friendship lasted throughout his lifetime. While working in Cesaris Atelier, it is likely that he painted still life and fruit. Cardinal Del Monte recognised his unique ability and became an important patron throughout his time in Rome.

At night, he carried a sword and frequented taverns and brothels. He was certainly heterosexual but may have been bisexual. Ambiguity about his sexuality is not surprising in view of the fact that, at the time, the penalty for sodomy was death and many offenders were hanged or burned alive. He roamed in the company of other young men, whose motto was *Nec Spe, Nec Metu* – without hope or fear. Easily insulted and taunted, these men frequently fought rival groups.

Onorio Longhi was the firebrand of Caravaggio's band. There was a large population of prostitutes in Rome at that time, one of whom was Fillide Melandroni, who had among her protectors, Ranuccio Tomassoni. Caravaggio painted Fillide's portrait on many occasions and she modelled for him for many of the religiously themed paintings that he produced at this point in his career.

It is clear that he was notoriously aggressive, if aggrieved and that he had a troubled personality, falling out with his friends on a regular basis. Some of this may have been due to a sense of insecurity as he lacked noble status. It has been suggested that he challenged an opponent to a sword fight but was dismissed as not worthy to dual with someone who was a papal knight. At that time, it had become an aspiration of many to become a Knight of Malta, which was a very prized title – its esteem enhanced by the religious fervour induced by the defeat of the Turks in the Siege of Malta.

Though his fame as a painter was bringing him significant commissions, including altar pieces, in 1606 he provoked a sword fight with Ranuccio Tomassoni. Opinion varies as to whether this was about a debt, a dispute about a tennis match or even the possibility that Caravaggio coveted Ranuccio's wife, Lavinia. Ranuccio was fatally wounded and Caravaggio himself received significant but not life-threatening wounds to the head.

A month elapsed before any charges were made, possibly to allow those involved to get clear of Rome. Initially, it was believed that, as the killing was not premeditated, Caravaggio would get off with a light sentence. The powerful Tomassoni family's influence prevailed however, and a death sentence was imposed on Caravaggio and banishment on his two seconds.

He fled to Naples, where he came under the protection of the powerful Colona family. He received many commissions, to the annoyance of his supporters in Rome. Clearly, many of these expected that a papal pardon would be granted more readily if he became a Knight of Malta. In any case, he suddenly left Naples and sailed to Malta.

The Grand Master of the order at that time was a French aristocrat, Alof De Wignacour, a man with considerable military experience who held a sumptuous court. Caravaggio's fame as a painter was known in Malta and he was soon introduced to Wignacour. He did several portraits of the Grand Master. In one these, it portrayed him in dramatic armour and another in knight's attire. Wignacour was delighted with these and awarded Caravaggio the Cross of Malta. However, entry to full knighthood had very strict criteria: specifically, anyone who had committed homicide was ineligible.

Wignacour pleaded Caravaggio's case with Pope Paul V and the Holy See. The Pope acceded to the petitions and despite his criminal record and lack of nobility, Caravaggio was appointed a magisterial knight in 1608. He had fulfilled the 12-month novitiate required before being professed, having been on the island exactly a year at that time. Each knight was obliged to pay a sizeable sum of passage (*Passagio*) money. It is likely that a commissioned painting of St John the Baptist was received as part payment of passage money.

Caravaggio, after a period of stability, again engaged in a fight, this time with another knight. He was said to have been imprisoned in an underground cell in the Castle St Angelo in Valletta. He supposedly escaped by means of a rope, boarded a ship and sailed to Sicily. It stretches credulity that he could have made such a seamless escape without inside help, as no knight was allowed to leave Malta without the expressed permission of the Grand Master.

In due course, a court case was held and Caravaggio, by reason of his non-appearance, was stripped of his knighthood. Despite this, he continued to describe himself as a knight throughout his time in Sicily. He appears to have become more agitated and paranoid and even describes himself as "Mad", at times, during this period. He continued to paint pictures for well-connected persons, including members of the Order of Malta. He also sent paintings to the Grand Master, presumably in an effort to regain his favour.

He returned to Naples, believing that a papal pardon was imminent. He was, by now, one of the foremost artists in Italy and his work was in great demand. He remained in fear of his life however and it must be understood that a death sentence, at that time, was equivalent to a Muslim fatwa. This meant that a Christian, anywhere, could be seen to administer justice by killing him.

During this time, he was attacked by four men and very seriously injured. While still suffering from the injuries he received in that fight, he received the news of his pardon and boarded a sailing ship for Rome. On board, he took several paintings intended for his long-term Roman patron, Cardinal Borghese. The boat put in to a small port Palo, where Caravaggio disembarked. Here, he was jailed for two days by the local Papal Guard and paid a substantial fee to be released. This may have been part of the pardon process.

Unfortunately, on his release, the sailing ship had left with his paintings on board. He travelled on, by foot and by sea, in the mid-summer heat and through mosquito infested regions. Reaching Port Ercole, the final destination of his original ship, he found it had been and gone. He developed fever and died, probably of dysentery complicated by malaria. He was 38 years of age.

Did He Suffer from Lead Poisoning?
Vincenti, said to be Italy's foremost cold case historian, revealed in 2010 that he had investigated the skeletal remains.

Caravaggio was interred in the San Sebastian Cemetery but, this had been built over in 1956. However, the bones had been moved to a local municipal cemetery and Vincenti identified a skeleton, which in all probability was that of the painter. DNA profile of a resident with a similar surname in Caravaggio's home time were 50-60% compatible.

Analysis of the skeleton showed toxic levels of lead in the bones. It is known that Caravaggio's palette included lead white and lead yellow. He would certainly have had long exposure to lead during his painting career. Some artists had a habit of licking their brushes to mould them into shape, thereby ingesting lead. It is suspected that Goya and Van Gough may also have suffered from lead poisoning.

Vincenti's findings were greeted sensationally. *The Guardian's* headline proclaimed, "The Mystery of Caravaggio's Death Solved at Last – painting killed him". Clearly, this is incorrect. Certainly, lead poisoning may have been a factor in his mood swings and aggressiveness but, the fact that he continued to paint right up to the time of his death makes it highly unlikely that he had significant peripheral neuropathy. Undoubtedly, the immediate cause of his death was a combination of dysentery, malaria and possibly sunstroke.

Supporting Evidence of Lead Poisoning

One of the clinical features of chronic lead poisoning is a blue line along the gums with bluish black edging to the teeth, known as Burton's Line. It is known that Caravaggio included many self-portraits in his paintings. The author has done a preliminary search of these for evidence of Burton's Line. In most of them the mouth is closed however, in *David with the Head of Goliath*, the severed head has its mouth open. It is generally accepted that the head of Goliath was a self-portrait by Caravaggio. It can be seen that the teeth in the lower gums are visible. While I cannot see a definite Burton's Line, the teeth are certainly blackened and, this would be in keeping with lead poisoning.

Renoir
Coping with Rheumatoid Arthritis

Pierre Auguste Renoir (1841-1919) was born in Limoges. One of five children, his father was a tailor. As a child, he drew on the apartment floor with his father's tailors chalk.

He suffered from rheumatoid arthritis for the last 25 years of his life. The disease was very aggressive for the final 15 years, leading to gross deformity of his hands and ultimately, he became confined to a wheelchair for the last seven years of his life. Despite this, he continued painting until the day before he died. His coping strategies were ahead of their day. His sunny personality allied to his coterie of devoted carers helped in his long struggle with the disease.

As a schoolboy, Renoir had singing lessons from Charles Gunot, who suggested a career in music. While he never lost his love of music (often singing as he painted and in adult life, he never moved residence without his piano), from the age of 12 he had decided on a career in painting.

From age 13 to 18 he was employed as a porcelain painter. In 1861, he joined Charles Gleyre's atelier, studying art with Monet, Sisley and Bazille. Through Monet, he met Pissarro and Cezanne. Albert and André Cezanne were to become lifelong, devoted friends. Gleyre, inspecting a sketch by him, is said to have remarked, "Young man, you are very skilful, very gifted but no doubt, you took up painting to amuse yourself."

Renoir replied, "Certainly, if it did not amuse me, I would not be doing it."

He was ambidextrous, continuing to paint with his left hand when he fractured the right in a cycling accident in 1897.

We are indebted to his second son, Jean for much of the intimate detail of his life. Jean was invalided home during the First World War. During this time, he wrote a biography of his father. Renoir had strong views on many topics.

"Learn to draw; it won't stop you becoming a genius," he would say.

Of hunting, he was disparaging, saying, "It requires carriages, society people, ridiculous clothes and even a poor fox and all that trouble with no more enjoyment than a game of marbles."

He always considered himself an artisan. When he became famous and people showered him with praise, he would say playfully, "Who? Me? A genius? What rot! I don't take drugs, I've never had syphilis, and I'm not a pederast ... well then?" His favourite painters were Watteau, Boucher and Fragonard. Like his fellow Impressionists, he struggled financially in his early years. He became the first of the group to achieve financial success. From 1881, the dealer, Durand-Ruel, began to find buyers for his work.

The onset of rheumatoid arthritis occurred in 1893, when he was 50 years old. Medical treatment comprised purges and the painkiller, antipyrine. He was reluctant to take antipyrine, fearing it would interfere with his creativity. Unimpressed at the value of walking, he concentrated on activities that would keep his arms and hands in best condition. He had wooden sticks made to order and juggled these for ten minutes each morning before going to the studio. He enjoyed playing billiards with his wife, Aline, as it forced him to adopt unusual positions. He played a French ball and stick game, bil-bouquet, in which a wooden ball with a hole in it is thrown in the air. The aim is to catch it on a stick threaded through the hole. He believed in the benefit of spa treatments and visited several, often staying several months. He always took his family with him and also, his parrot and his beloved piano.

The disease became more aggressive and disabling in the decade from age 60 to 70. Over this period, he developed ankylosis of his shoulder and spontaneous rupture of extensor tendons in his hands. Walking became difficult due to arthritis in his feet. His hands became progressively more deformed. Over this decade, he would have his hands bandaged to prevent maceration. Contrary to many reports, these bandages were never used to secure the brushes. He continued to hold the brushes between his fingers. He used shorter brush strokes but the end result were paintings in which experts are unable to see technical differences from those he executed prior to the onset of disease.

He had a Bells' palsy, which was treated by electrotherapy. Over this period, he lost weight despite a good appetite, dropping to 46kg. He had rheumatoid nodules surgically removed from his back.

His family doctor was now Dr Gachet, famously painted by Van Gough. In 1912, at the age of 71, he was said to have suffered a stroke affecting his arms and legs. It is now speculated that it was his cervical spine disease that caused the weakness. From then on, he was confined to a wheelchair. He also had a sedan chair, in which he could be carried over terrain unsuitable to a wheelchair. Despite multiple cushions, he had difficulty finding a comfortable position. By now, he had moved to the south of France, to avail of the warm climate. Even there, he had himself wrapped up in shawls. He encouraged the household cats to nestle on his lap and warm him. Interestingly, the Institute Pasteur have identified cat hairs in some paintings of that period.

No longer able to hold his palette, he balanced it between his knees and the easel but, later had it attached to the arm of his wheelchair. He devised a system whereby unstretched canvas was fixed to wooden slats, which passed over two rollers, one near the ground and the other at seven feet. By cranking a handle, the apparatus fixed to a bicycle chain could be moved up and down, enabling any section of a large canvas to be positioned within his reach. It replaced his easel.

His son, Jean, describes the family distress each morning, watching this pale, deformed, pain-wracked man and listening to his groans as he adjusted himself in his wheelchair but, Renoir would then set the mood. When being handed his brushes, he would wink and say, "That one over there; no, the other one."

He would dip his brush in turpentine, look at the subject matter and place a mark of rose madder on the blank canvas. Then, with another wink and a smile say, "Jean, open the yellow curtains a little more."

As Jean put it, "Another day of happiness would begin for Renoir."

His beloved wife, Aline, who had devoted her life to him, died in 1915, causing him great distress. His youngest son, Coco, then 14 years old, took on his care when staff left at night. He became very dependent on Coco and, in order to see him as much as possible, had a teacher come to the house to tutor him He taught Coco the art of ceramics.

He started sculpting in the last twelve years of his life. When no longer physically able to sculpt, he instructed his assistant sculptors, Richard Guino and Marcel Gimond how to fashion the clay to his requirements.

In 1918, he is said to have developed gangrene in a foot. In 1919, despite excellent care, he developed bed sores and in November of that year, he died of pneumonia. He painted a still life of apples in a basket the day before he died. As his brushes were removed, he said, "I think I am beginning to understand some of it."

Further Reading
Pierre Auguste Renoir; mon pere by Jean Renoir (Gallimard, Paris. 1981)

"How Renoir Coped with Rheumatoid Arthritis" by Boonen, Annelies et al in *British Medical Journal* (1997), 315:1704-1708

Mozart

His Death and Burial

Controversy surrounds Mozart's final illness, leading to death aged 35 years and, burial. Was he poisoned and if so by whom? Could it have been Salieri, his "rival" at court or Süssmayr, his collaborator? Was it the Freemasons, as Mozart might have revealed secret Masonic rituals in *Die Zauberflote* (The Magic Flute)? Or, less sensationally, did he die of natural causes following an acute attack of rheumatic fever, complicated by uraemia and hastened by the medical treatment he received, especially venesection? The fact that his final year (1791) was filled with activity, makes it clear that he certainly did not suffer from chronic poisoning.

The film, *Amadeus*, highlighted his supposed rivalry with Salieri. The truth seems to be that their relationship was one of mutual respect. Salieri had come to Vienna in 1766, becoming Court Composer in 1774 and Court Kapellmeister in 1788. Mozart came to Vienna in 1781 as a freelance musician. He left his post in Salzburg as he felt his musical ambitions, especially towards opera, were being stifled there. He petitioned, unsuccessfully, for the creation of a second post as Kapellmeister when Joseph II died. Such a post would have assured him of an annual income of 2000 florin. As Leopold II, Joseph's brother and successor, had 16 children, he no doubt hoped at least to get a post as music teacher to the royal children.

In April 1791, he petitioned Vienna City Council for the post of Cathedral Kapellmeister at St Stephens and in May, was appointed unpaid assistant to that post. Despite the rejection of his petition, he travelled with Constanze, his wife and Süssmayr, his collaborator to attend Leopold's coronation as Holy Roman Emperor in Frankfurt. This was an expensive trip and suggests he was still hopeful of getting a Royal Commission. That year, he turned down a lucrative project in London, citing Constanzes' health as the reason. In mid-July, she returned from Baden, where she was "taking the cure". She was due with their sixth child. Franz Xavier Wolfgang was born on 26 July. In nine years of marriage, she had born him six children.

He did receive a commission to write an opera in celebration of Leopold's coronation as King of Bohemia. The resulting opera was *La Clemenza de Tito*. On the opening night, the performance was delayed by an hour, due to Leopold's late arrival at the theatre. Leopold's wife, who appears to have blocked Mozart's appointment as music teacher to her children, is reported to have shouted, "German hogwash!" from the Royal Box at the end of the opera. Perceived Royal disfavour meant the opera was poorly attended during the ongoing festivities.

Despite this, *La Clemenza de Tito* gained great public support and became the most popular Mozart opera for the last half of the 19th century. In retrospect, it was an opera written in a hurry, by a sick man more preoccupied with *The Magic Flute*, which premiered in Vienna in the same month. Change in taste now sees *Clemenza* downgraded to beta status, with *The Magic Flute* being rated an alpha by Forman.

About this time, he received another commission – to write a requiem by an "anonymous" patron. This patron was, in fact, Count Franz Walsegg-Stuppach, who wanted the piece as a memorial to his wife, who had died suddenly in 1791. The Count commissioned pieces from several composers and attempted to pass them off as his own work. (Stuppach later created uproar when Constanze tried to get the *Requiem* published after Mozart's death, claiming sole ownership of the work).

On 18 November 1791, Mozart conducted a piece (*Kliene Freimaurer Kantante*) he had written to celebrate the dedication of a new temple for his Freemason Lodge. Two days later, he was confined to bed, where he remained for the final 15 days of his life. Initially, his hands and feet swelled and, he was in great pain. During this period, he would have been physically unable to write the score. However, his pupils, Eybler and Süssmayr, were in attendance and almost certainly collaborated in composing the *Requiem*.

His doctors prescribed emetics and cold compresses. Most debilitatingly, they performed repeated venesection. Constanze was frantic with worry and asked her sister, Sophie Weber, to arrange a visit by a priest. Her sister later recounted hearing Mozart discuss with Süssmayr how the *Requiem* should be completed after his death. His last recorded movement is said to have been an attempt to describe the drum roll in the *Requiem*.

He died during the night of December 4th to 5th. Constanze was left widowed, essentially without income, to raise their two surviving children, both boys, one aged seven years and the other not yet six months. It comes as no surprise that she was so distraught, she did not have the strength to attend the funeral service in St Stephens.

His Burial
To understand the reality of burial practice when Mozart died, it is essential to know the practices Joseph II had introduced. These were based on Joseph's observations in France and made good public health sense.

He ordered the closure of all burial sites within the city limits. He decreed that new graveyards be opened well outside the city boundaries. Concerned at the slow rate of decomposition, he forbade burial in coffins. Bodies were to be buried having been sewn into linen sacks. Coffins were permitted for the purpose of transporting bodies from church to cemetery but, were to be reusable. Plots were to be dug six feet deep and four feet wide. Each plot could receive up to six bodies: four adults and two children. The bodies were to be strewn with unslaked lime to speed decomposition. While it was still allowed for a body to be taken initially to a church, after prayers and music, "it shall be conveyed by the priest, without ceremony, to an outlying cemetery for interment."

By the time Mozart's body reached St Marx cemetery, it was dark. The body was kept overnight in a small mortuary and buried next day, 7 December.

The question of an unmarked grave would not have arisen, as Josephin decrees also stated that memorials were only allowed on the cemetery walls and not on the graves themselves. Meeting an unexpected level of popular resistance, the total ban on coffin burial was being relaxed at the time of Mozart's death. However, all non-aristocrats had to be buried in these distant cemeteries.

Contrary to subsequent legend, Mozart was not buried unnoticed and unheralded in a pauper's grave. While Mozart died without means, Constanze managed to pay off all his debts. An exception was made and she was granted a small state pension. Gottfried Van Swieten and Baroness Thun, who were family friends, helped finance the education of his two sons. After his death, memorial concerts were held to give Constanze financial help. The Freemasons held collections for her. Count Wallsegg-Stuppach, in an about turn, arranged a public performance of the *Requiem*, which brought in more than 300 ducats for Constanze. A huge memorial service was held in Prague, where the bells were rung for half an hour.

Conclusion

Mozart died from natural causes. He expired as a result of streptococcal septicaemia complicated by uraemia and heart failure. His death was hastened by excessive venesection. There is no evidence he was poisoned maliciously. He was a known consumer of over the shelf patent remedies, some of which contained antimony. Such medications were freely available at the time. He was buried according to the customs of his day. He was not buried in a pauper's grave. He did not die unnoticed and unheralded.

Further Reading

Mozart in Vienna, 1781-1791 by Volkmar Brannbehreus (Andre Deutsch, London. 1990)

The Good Opera Guide by Denis Forman (Weidenfeld & Nicolson, London. 1994)

Charles Darwin

Common Illness, Uncommon Man

Charles Darwin suffered ill health most of his adult life. Paradoxically, this may have helped rather than hindered his work, by isolating him from social life and the teaching and administration associated with a normal scientific career.

He consulted up to twenty doctors, including William Jenner and Henry Bence Jones. He was prescribed the medications of the day, including Fowler's solution, which contained arsenic. Many and varied diagnoses have been proposed to explain his symptoms. These include Chagas disease, cyclical vomiting, Crohn's disease and panic disorder. He was almost certainly suffering from chronic gastritis as a result of Helicobacter pylori infection. Shanahan argues cogently that his myriad symptoms largely fit in the spectrum of irritable bowel syndrome (IBS).

Overlaying any physical problem was his fear that his theory of evolution would destroy himself, his wife and family in intolerant Victorian England.

Darwin was born in 1809, son of the physician, Robert Darwin and Susannah Wedgewood. He was the fifth of six children. His mother died when he was eight years old and he was reared primarily by his three older sisters. At age nine, he was sent to boarding school with his brother, Erasmus. He became an apprentice doctor to his father at age 16.

With Erasmus, he was enrolled as a medical student in Edinburgh. He found the medical course was not to his liking. He described surgery as "brutal" and was upset at the sight of blood. Increasingly, he was drawn to other pursuits, learning taxidermy and studying natural history. His father despaired and removed him from Edinburgh, enrolling him in Cambridge. The plan was now that Charles would pursue an Arts degree, with the long-term aim of taking orders and becoming a country parson.

He attended Christ's College to take an ordinary pass degree. He collected beetles as well as partaking in shooting and fishing. He completed his degree in January 1831 but was obliged to complete two further terms in Cambridge. One benefit of this was a lifelong affinity for early rising – a habit then said to distinguish Cambridge students from those in Oxford!

Reluctant to take Holy Orders, he planned to go on an expedition to Tenerife, to study natural history with classmates later that year. Henslow, a botanist in Cambridge, in the meantime had recommended him as gentleman naturalist to travel on the planned two-year voyage of the *Beagle*, mapping the coast of South America. He was invited to join the expedition in August. He was to be funded by his uncle, Josiah Wedgewood.

The captain of the *Beagle*, Robert FitzRoy, was well aware of the strains of command, which had led his predecessor, Pringle Stokes, to committing suicide by shooting himself. He planned to share his accommodation with Darwin to afford himself some social interaction with a gentleman while at sea.

When they reached South America, Darwin would be free to spend prolonged periods ashore. Awaiting embarkation, Darwin suffered chest pain and palpitations but told no one, in case it might prevent him from travelling. When they sailed, he had severe sea sickness. He returned to England in 1835 and in 1839, married his first cousin, Emma Wedgewood, with whom he had ten children.

Illness and Symptomatology
Symptoms began about two years after his return to England. He suffered headache, vertigo, tremors and fainting. In addition, he had bouts of vomiting, colic, bloating and abdominal pain.

Frequently, he had a sensation of impending death. All symptoms were aggravated by excitement or stress. He relied heavily on Emma in these attacks. He nicknamed her "Mammy", leading to the suggestion that she was always the mother and never the child, while Darwin was always the child and never the father.

When conventional medicine failed him in 1849, he turned to the then fashionable water therapy. He found the strict spa regimen helped and despite having no faith in them, took homeopathic medicines. He had intermittent water treatment over the next decade in various establishments. He had a walk constructed in the grounds of his residence and stuck rigidly to early rising, diet, exercise and limited hours of work.

Into this mix came the pressure of religious belief. When in Cambridge, Darwin took a relaxed attitude to religion but, nevertheless attended church eight times a week! The Wedgewoods were Unitarians while Darwin's father was Anglican. Unitarians believed reformers had not gone far enough. They found inspiration in the Bible and had no imposed doctrine. Darwin realised that evolutionists of any kind were likely to be perceived as radicals seeking to overthrow society. Espousing such views could conceivably lead to a charge of blasphemy.

As to possible physical illness, Adler proposed that Darwin had contracted Chagas disease. When, on one of his land expeditions in Argentina, Darwin described being bitten by the great black bug of the pampas. This bug was likely Triatoma infestans, the vector for Trypanosoma cruzi. While it might explain his gastric symptoms and, with a good stretch of the imagination, his late cardiac symptoms, there is much against this diagnosis. Specifically, he did not develop symptoms of megaoesophagus or megacolon.

He lived to the relatively old age, for his time, of 73 and indeed, his symptoms lessened with age. He did not suffer weight loss. Crohn's disease has been proposed but is highly unlikely. Marshall posits that he was infected with Helicobacter pylori, leading to chronic gastritis. This is probable but, it would not explain many of the extra gastric symptoms. Cyclical vomiting syndrome was proposed by Hayman. Darwin's symptoms were not cyclical, as evidenced by his regular diary entries.

The most convincing explanation of his illness is that of Shanahan, who proposes that the disorder is in the spectrum of functional dyspepsia and irritable bowel disease (IBS). It is possible that gastrointestinal infection triggered the IBS. Comorbid extra-intestinal somatisation could explain his non-gastrointestinal symptoms. The author thinks it likely that Darwin had underlying diverticular disease.

Darwin had a multiplicity of symptoms. Severe problems began two years after his return from the *Beagle* expedition. These severely limited his social interactions. Paradoxically, this allowed him to concentrate on his scientific work. While his father may have been overbearing, he had a most supportive wife. It is probable that he had gastritis due to Helicobacter infection. A compelling case can be made that he suffered from irritable bowel syndrome (IBS). He may well have had diverticular disease. It is unlikely that he suffered from Chagas disease.

Addendum

FitzRoy, captain of the *Beagle*, pioneered the science of meteorology. When Finisterre (the sea area that was used in shipping forecasts by the BBC since 1949) was renamed in 2002, it was called FitzRoy. Sadly, Robert FitzRoy emulated his uncle, Viscount Castlereagh and self-destructed by cutting his throat at age 63.

Further Reading

"Darwinian dyspepsia: an extraordinary scientist, an ordinary illness, great dignity" by F. Shanahan in *The American Journal of Gastroenterology* (2012), 107:161-164

"Darwin's Illness" by Saul Adler in *Nature* (1959), 184: 1102-1103

"Darwin's Illness was Helicobacter Pylori" by Barry J. Marshall in barryjmarshall.blogspot.com (13 February 2009)

"Darwin's Illness Revisited" by John A. Hayman in *British Medical Journal* (2009), 339: 1413-5

Seacole vs. Nightingale

A Crimean Odyssey: Separating Fact from Fiction

A Lady with a Lamp shall stand
In the great history of the land
– Henry Wadsworth Longfellow

See. Here is Mary Seacole, who did as much in the Crimea
as / Another magic-lamping Lady, but, being dark, could
scarce be / Seen for Florence's candle – **Salman Rushdie**

In recent times, Florence Nightingale's reputation has suffered unfairly when compared to Mary Seacole. While Nightingale has always had her detractors, much of the promotion of Seacole, at her expense, is uncritical and inaccurate.

Seacole, a Jamaican, was voted in top place of 100 great Black Britons in 2004. Undoubtedly many have felt constrained at challenging the myths about her, for fear of being accused of racial bias. Sadly, the Nursing Standard, owned by the Royal College of Nursing, has published many false or exaggerated claims, including one that Seacole "changed the face of modern nursing." However, Seacole was not a nurse and never claimed to be one. She described herself as a "doctress" and credited her mother for training her as a Creole herbalist.

Nightingale, by contrast, has suffered from the popular sport of debunking heroines – especially Victorian ones with a perceived privileged background. Both women deserve recognition and praise for their work in the Crimea. However, it is time to assess their respective contributions in a calm and unbiased way.

In the early 19th century, hospitals had a dreadful reputation. It was said that patients, on hearing of an impending admission to hospital, gave themselves up as lost. Nursing was looked down on and was largely unstructured and unregulated. Dickens' Sairey Gamp and Betsey Prig were exaggerated versions of the untrained nurses of the day.

In Catholic countries, trained nurses were largely members of religious orders, such as the Sisters of Charity founded by Vincent de Paul, Sisters of Mercy founded by Catherine McAuley and the Irish Sisters of Charity founded by Mary Aikenhead. The latter two orders sent nuns to Paris to train under the Daughters of Charity.

Florence Nightingale, born in Florence to a wealthy English family, had a vision at age 17 that she was destined to serve mankind. She was 31 years of age before her family agreed to her training as a nurse. She trained briefly in Kaiserwerth and then with the Daughters of Charity in Paris. Back in London, she was appointed Superintendent of the Establishment for Gentlewomen during illness and later, to a similar post at King's College Hospital.

Nightingale was a sanitarian who believed in scrupulous cleanliness. In keeping with medical beliefs of the time, she was also a miasmatist who believed stagnant air spread disease.

The Crimean War began in 1854. Conditions were appalling at the British base in Scutari, across the Bosporus from Istanbul. By contrast, the French had their Sisters of Charity in their hospitals. There was a public outcry in Britain. Nightingale volunteered her services and Sidney Herbert, Secretary of War, dispatched her with 38 nurses, (including 10 Catholic nuns) to Scutari, where invalided soldiers were cared for in filthy, rat-infested barracks. Field Surgeons treated war wounds with debridement and amputation. If fever other than malaria supervened, doctors had little to treat them. Soldiers designated as having a medical illness were ferried from Crimea to Scutari, a journey of at least three days. Many died on the transport ships. It was said that soldiers were not sent to Scutari to be healed but to die.

Fevers were variously called "Crimean Fever" or "Varna Fever". Most patients were diagnosed with "febris continua communa" to distinguish it from typhus or "high fever". Overcrowding lead to the spread of typhus, dysentery, typhoid and respiratory infections. Nightingale introduced washing of patients. She gave them clean beds and clothes. She arranged the disposal of human waste and had windows that opened installed. Her mantra was fresh air, warmth, cleanliness and a good diet.

In improving patients' diet, she was helped greatly by another volunteer, the French chef, Alexis Bénoit Soyer. Soyer was head chef at the Reform Club in London. During the Irish Famine, he was seconded to Dublin at the request of Lord Bessborough, the Lord Lieutenant, to set up soup kitchens. He returned to London and ran his own restaurant before volunteering to join Nightingale in Scutari, spurred on by an imploring letter to him in *The Times*.

At the time, soldiers were given a daily ration and left to their own devices to prepare the food. Soyer centralised cooking, inventing the mobile field oven whose basic design was still in use in the British Army during the Gulf War, a century later. He set up a bakery on board a ship that supplied fresh bread to the hospital daily. He invented the Scutari teapot – a tall kettle with a detachable strainer for the leaves. Essentially, he founded the Catering Corps of the British Army. When Nightingale sailed to the Crimean Peninsula in May 1855, Soyer accompanied her to Balaklava.

Mary Seacole (née Grant) was born in Kingston, Jamaica. She described herself as Creole and was proud of her Scotch blood, inherited from her Scottish soldier father. Her mother was free Jamaican and Mary was legally classified as a Mulatto. It has been suggested that she was, in reality, a Quadroon (three quarters) white.

As the educated daughter of a white officer and free Jamaican mother with a successful business, she would have had a respected position in Jamaican society. Though proud of her black ancestry, she described herself as "only a little brown."

She married Horatio Seacole, said to be godson of Admiral Horatio Nelson. After the deaths of her husband and mother, she took over the running of her mother's boarding house, Blundell Hall. She treated victims of a major cholera epidemic in 1850. A year later, when visiting her brother in Panama, there was an outbreak of cholera there and she found her services in demand, due to her previous experience of the disease. Her treatment included mustard rubs, poultices, rehydration and, alarmingly, lead acetate.

She travelled back and forth in the Caribbean. On a visit home to Jamaica in 1853, she experienced racial discrimination being refused passage on an American ship. On arrival, she was asked to assist in managing an outbreak of yellow fever by the medical authorities. She later returned to Panama where, hearing of the outbreak of war in the Crimea, she decided to go to England again to deal with her gold mining investments and volunteer as a nurse.

Nightingale's first tranche of nurses had already been selected and dispatched. Seacole attempted to join the second contingent without success. She applied to the War Office and the Crimean Fund for support, also without success. Her age (she was almost 50) and her lack of testimonials were a problem but, it is probable that her colour told against her.

She then sailed for the Crimea independently to follow the family business and set up the "British Hotel" in Balaklava, planned as "a mess table and comfortable quarters for sick and convalescent officers." She stopped off in Scutari, where Nightingale treated her kindly and provided overnight accommodation.

She opened her British Hotel in March 1855. Soyer, the French chef was an early visitor. His business advice to her included concentrating on catering and not to provide overnight accommodation. Seacole catered primarily for the officer class in her hotel. She was however, apparently held in high esteem by the rank and file, being known as "Mother Seacole". As well as selling provisions to the troops, she was known for her kindness and generosity to those unable to pay.

She claimed, in her memoirs, to have been the first British woman to enter Sevastopol after it fell to the Allies. Her memoirs recall that she distributed refreshments to the injured troops awaiting evacuation. She also dislocated her thumb on another occasion, attending troops under fire.

After the fall of Sevastopol, her business initially prospered as she catered for picnics, theatre events and horse racing. As the war drew to a close however, she ran into financial difficulties with an oversupply of goods that she had to sell off cheaply. She was pursued by creditors and on her return to Britain, was declared bankrupt. A testimony to the esteem she was held in was the setting up of several public funds to help her out of financial difficulties. These were supported by some of the top British military figures of the day.

Her intention had been to volunteer for service in India during the Indian Mutiny in 1857. She was dissuaded from this venture by Lord Panmure the new Secretary of War due to her ongoing financial troubles and failing health. The same year, she published a lively memoir called *Wonderful Adventures of Mrs Seacole in Many Lands*.

Mary Seacole was a kind, generous, adventurous and brave woman. She was loved by the troops who affectionately called her "Mother Seacole". Her time in Crimea was spent entirely on the Crimean Peninsula. She was often near the front lines. By contrast, Nightingale was based in Scutari, across the Bosporus from Istanbul, three days by ship from Crimea.

But Scutari was also a dangerous place. Many doctors and nurses died there, as well as soldiers. Nightingale herself got "Crimean Fever" and, was fortunate to survive albeit, with long-term damage to her health. It is disingenuous to portray her as living a sheltered life, far removed from the front lines. After the Crimean War, Nightingale campaigned vigorously to raise the reputation of nursing.

Seacole's role in advancing the nursing profession and, her medical expertise, have been highly exaggerated in recent times. Perhaps the search for a black heroine has blinded many to reality.

Both Seacole and Nightingale deserve recognition in their own ways. Promoting Seacole as a rival to Nightingale does a disservice to the history of nursing. The siting of a memorial statue to Seacole in the grounds of St Thomas' Hospital, where Nightingale's School of Nursing was founded, appears deliberately provocative.

Further Reading
"Florence Nightingale and Mary Seacole: Nursings Bitter Rivalry" by Lynn McDonald in *History Today* (2012), 69.9

Ignaz Semmelweis
Hungarian Medical Icon

Ignaz Semmelweis was born to the wife of a well-to-do grocer in Budapest, in 1818. He has become an iconic medical figure in his native Hungary. No visit to Budapest is complete without a visit to the Semmelweis Museum, which is located in his family home. While there is much to fascinate there, the author found the exhibits random and poorly explained. Some of the myths that have grown up about Semmelweis are also perpetuated there.

He qualified in Medicine in Vienna in 1844. In 1846, he took up a post in Obstetrics in the Vienna General Hospital. At that time, "childbed fever" was rampant.

Semmelweis noted that Ward 1 had a maternal mortality rate of 29% whereas, where hands were washed in ward 2 the mortality rate was 3%. In Ward 1, deliveries were performed by medical students and in Ward 2, by midwifery students. When, at his instigation the attendants switched wards, the high mortality followed the medical students. As medical students also performed autopsies, he suggested they may be introducing some toxic material from the dead bodies into the women in the course of delivery.

Alexander Gordon, in 1795 in Aberdeen, had posited the introduction of "putrid matter" into the uterus by persons performing delivery. He advised handwashing before attendance at a confinement. Oliver Wendell Holmes, in Boston in 1843, had set forth his view that childbed fever was an infection caused by "germs" transmitted by those attending a confinement. Holmes suggested that a doctor should not attend a confinement until 24 hours after performing an autopsy. He also suggested a change of clothes and washing of hands in chlorinated water. Two of the most influential American obstetricians, Meigs and Hodge, directly rebutted Homes, stating childbed fever was neither contagious nor transmitted by doctors but rather being the result of "miasma".

In 1847, Jacob Kolletschka, the Professor of Forensic Medicine in Vienna, cut his finger while performing an autopsy and died of septicaemia. Semmelweis recognised that the findings in Kolletschka's autopsy report were identical to those seen in women who died of childbed fever and made the connection to the professor's cut finger. As medical students came to the delivery room directly from performing autopsies, he concluded that they were transmitting putrid material that caused the fever. He ordered handwashing in chlorinated water prior to attendance at a confinement and, the mortality fell dramatically.

Despite this, he encountered much resistance from his colleagues. He did not publish his work immediately and was bypassed for a permanent post in Vienna. He resigned and returned to Budapest, becoming Head of Obstetrics in St Rochus Hospital in 1851. He introduced chlorine disinfection and the mortality from childbed fever fell to less than 1%. In 1861, he published *Die Aetiologe, der Begriff und die Prophylaxis des Kindbettfiebers* (The Cause, Concept and Prophylaxis of Childbed Fever).

Contrary to legend, he spent many years happily practising in Budapest. He was however, known to be stubborn and self-righteous. It could well be that his failure to secure a permanent post in Vienna left him with some understandable bitterness. He certainly was furious with the negative reviews of his book, to the extent that he collected them for a pamphlet, published in 1862.

In the years that followed, he suffered from failing memory, depression and paranoia. In 1865, his family had him committed to a Viennese mental institution. Two weeks later, he was dead of infection, probably the result of injuries sustained from being restrained by hospital attendants. There seems to be no truth in the suggestion that this was streptococcal septicaemia. It has been suggested that his mental deterioration could have been due to Alzheimer's or other organic dementia.

Ignaz Semmelweis's legacy has been complicated by many myths and half-truths. Morton Thompson, in his 1949 novel, *The Cry and the Covenant*, based on the life of Semmelweis, perpetuated the image of a frustrated medical pioneer ridiculed by his colleagues. Many of the quotes about him, attributed to other pioneering scientists, are often misrepresentations of what was actually said. However, even stripped of myth, the story of Semmelweis is still an astonishing one. It is one of good clinical perception with perseverance and conviction. There is no doubting the reality that his observation and practice led to significant reduction in maternal mortality. He deserves his place as an iconic figure in medical history.

Afterword

Puerperal fever is still recorded in over 200 women annually in the USA. Mortality is highest when infection becomes evident within four days of delivery. Toxic Shock Syndrome is caused by a Group A Streptococcus, with an incidence of 3.5 per 100,000 and can occur in post-partum states.

Further Reading

"Searching for Semmelweis" by Barron H. Lerner in *The Lancet* (2014), 383; 210-212

Marie Skłodowska Curie

The Scientist who Triumphed over Misogyny
and Xenophobia

Marie Skłodowska Curie is probably the world's most famous female scientist. She succeeded despite extreme misogyny and xenophobia. Amongst other achievements, she was the first woman to win a Nobel Prize, the first female professor in the University of Paris and the first person to win two Nobel Prizes in different disciplines. Nevertheless, this giant of the scientific world also had a human side, falling in love three times.

Born into the Russian segment of a Poland divided also with Prussia and Austria, she remained a fervent Polish nationalist all her life. She named the first chemical element that she discovered, Polonium, taught her children her native language and employed Polish governesses to teach them.

She was born in the New Town area of Warsaw on Freta Street. Her young eyes would have gazed on the surrounding churches of St Jacek, St Francis, the Holy Spirit and St Kazimierz's. Copper-domed St Kazimierz's was built for the Sisters of the Sacrament, a silent order. They were to break that vow for the first time in 300 years when they converted the crypt into a hospital during the Warsaw Rising of 1944. The consequences were catastrophic when the Nazis crushed the uprising.

Maria, her birth name, was the youngest of five children. She was born in 1867. Her family had lost much of their property and wealth as a result of their involvement in Polish nationalism. The most recent "January Uprising" had only finally been suppressed by Russia in 1864. Bismarck's decision to put railways in Prussianadministered Poland at the disposal of the Russian troop movements, elevated the rising into a war against Russia. Following this revolt, it was decreed that all school subjects, other than Religious Instruction, be taught in Russian, which was also to become the official language of Russian-administered Poland. Maria's father was dismissed from his teaching post. Her sister, Zofia, died when she was seven and her mother when she was ten years of age.

Denied higher education due to her gender, with her sister Bronislawa, she enrolled in the underground "Flying University". Bronislawa later moved to Paris to study medicine, with the understanding that Maria would follow when finances permitted. In the meantime, she took on a governess post in Szczuki with the wealthy Zorowski family, who were distantly related. While there, she fell in love with their son, Kaziemierz. His parents opposed the union, which they perceived to be with a penniless relative. Kaziemierz did not or could not stand up to them. His failure to do so left her heartbroken and in despair. Later, she wrote to her cousin, "If men do not want to marry impecunious girls, let them go to the devil."

She returned to Warsaw and finally, in 1891, moved to Paris. In Paris, she adopted the French version of her name, Marie. She lived in straightened circumstances, attending the University of Paris. In 1893, she obtained a degree in Physics and the following year, one in Chemistry. She studied the magnetic properties of metals, her supervisor being Pierre Curie. In 1894, he proposed marriage but, she refused, as she planned to return to Poland. Smitten, he offered to move to Poland. In the event, she was denied a place in Krakow because of her gender.

Pierre persuaded her to return to Paris to pursue a PhD. She had badgered the somewhat otherworldly Pierre to complete his own PhD on magnetism. Both loved science, travel and cycling. In 1895, they married. Their daughters, Irene and Eve, were born, respectively, in 1897 and 1904.

Her studies led her to believe that, as yet unknown elements, more powerful than Uranium, existed. She employed a physically demanding distillation process to the Uranium containing pitchblende. She conducted the research in a makeshift laboratory, housed in an abandoned medical dissecting room. Her first publication on pitchblende was presented to the Academie des Science on her behalf by Gabriel Lippmann.

In 1898, she discovered that Thorium emitted rays. Pierre was so intrigued that he gave up his own work and joined her. That year, they jointly published a paper describing a new element, Polonium. The same year, they described another element they called Radium. About this time, they coined the term radioactivity. The finding that Radium could destroy tumour cells was serendipitous. She would later make a point of stressing that when she discovered Radium, there was no reason to expect it to have such an application. She would point out that scientific work should not be considered from the point of view of the direct usefulness of it – it should be done for itself.

In 1903, they were invited to a talk on radioactivity by the Royal Institution in London. Being a woman, Marie was not allowed address the Institution and the presentation was given solely by Pierre. They did not patent their discovery. She would later say, "There were no patents: Radium was not to enrich anyone; radium belongs to the people."

This lack of patent was later shamelessly exploited to sell to a gullible public, products as diverse as toothpaste, cosmetics and aphrodisiacs such as the "Scrotal Radiendocrinator".

In December 1903, they were awarded the Nobel Prize jointly with Henri Becquerel. Initially, the Nobel Committee intended to honour only Pierre and Henri but, tipped off by a member of the committee, Pierre objected and Marie's name was added. She became the first woman to receive a Nobel prize. Over the next eleven years, they pursued a back-breaking schedule of research, publication, teaching and travel.

The marriage and joint work came to a sudden end in 1906, when Pierre died. On a rainy day in Paris, on the Rue Dauphine, his skull was crushed when he was knocked down by a horse-drawn vehicle. She was offered and accepted appointment to his chair, becoming the first female professor in the University of Paris. Devastated by Pierre's death, she plunged herself into work and her father-in-law, Eugene, took over the care of her children.

In 1910, she finally isolated Radium and defined the international unit for radioactive emissions, which was later named the curie (Ci).

In 1911, she ran for a vacant seat in the French Academy of Sciences. Vilified in the French press as a foreigner and an atheist, she lost, by two votes, to Edourd Branly. Branly's trump cards were being French and male.

She had fallen in love again, this time with Pierre Langevin, a married man and former close associate of her late husband. Somehow her love letters were leaked to the press. They had a field day describing her as a Polish Jew (she was not Jewish) who had broken up a happy French marriage (he was estranged). Einstein gave her much appreciated moral support at this time. Despite the scandal, the Nobel Committee honoured her a second time, at the end of 1911, awarding her the Nobel Prize in Chemistry.

She had, what is described as, a physical and psychological collapse a month later and spent time recovering with her friend, Hertha Ayrton, a suffragist and electrical engineer in England. She did not return to work for a year.

In 1913, she visited Poland again, being made welcome in Warsaw but largely ignored by the Russian authorities.

On the outbreak of war in 1914, she set up a series of mobile x-ray units to assist surgeons in the treatment of wounded soldiers. She later introduced radon needles to treat infected wounds. Assisted by her daughter, Irene and a military doctor, she set up x-ray facilities at frontline field hospitals. The dangers of x-rays were not appreciated and her exposure undoubtedly contributed to later overt radiation sickness.

An estimated one million soldiers used the units. Despite this, she got no formal recognition from the French government. Though she had discovered Radium she was no longer able to afford to buy it in sufficient quantities to equip the institute she was developing in Paris. She approached the French government for the funding but was refused.

Reluctantly, she accepted an invitation to visit the USA in 1921, to raise funds for research on Radium. The trip was a great financial success but, as always, she insisted funds be used only for the Institute in Paris. She met President Warren Harding, who presented her with one gram of Radium purchased with these monies. Her Institute in Paris went on to produce four more Nobel Prize winners, including her daughter, Irene and her son-in-law, Frederick Joliet in 1935.

She made another fundraising visit to the USA in 1929, to raise money for the proposed Radium institute in Warsaw. In 1932, she opened the Warsaw Institute. The Polish capital was, perhaps, at its zenith in science and innovation then. Notables there included Kazimierz Funk, discoverer of the B vitamins; mathematician, Stefan Mazurkiewicz; pioneering microscopist, Jerzy Nomarski and inventors, Józef Kosacki and Rudolf Gundlach. This was the city that Hitler later decreed should be razed to the ground – "Glattraziert" – and Himmler referred to as "that great abscess".

Marie was now in declining health. She made a final visit to Poland early in 1934. Later that year, she died of aplastic anaemia in her adoptive France.

Marie Curie was one of the greatest scientists the world has seen. She received two Nobel Prizes, becoming the first woman to achieve the distinction. She was the first person to be awarded the Nobel Prize in two different disciplines. She was the first female Professor in the University of Paris. Her Institute in Paris went on to produce four further Nobel Laureates, including her daughter, Irene.

These achievements were made in the face of huge discrimination regarding her race and gender. Her family suffered privation at the hands of the state by refusing to eschew their Polish nationalism. She also remained fiercely patriotic, calling the first element she identified, Polonium. As well as founding a Radium Institute, in Paris she achieved her wish to have one built in Warsaw.

She worked hard to save French lives in World War I and to make Paris a centre of excellence in radiation research. Despite this, she received scant recognition as an individual from the French state. Though she outlived Pierre by almost three decades and, independently received a second Nobel Prize, virtually all state recognition has been in their joint names.

She payed the ultimate price, dying as a result of exposure to radiation in the course of her work. Sixty years after her death, she was reinterred with Pierre in the Parthenon in Paris. A remarkable human being and scientist, her friend, Albert Einstein opined that she was the only person he knew who could not be corrupted by fame.

Further Reading

"Marie Curie: A Life in Science" by Patricia Fara in *History Today* (2017), vol 67 p36-47

Warsaw 1944 by Alexandra Richie (William Collins, London. 2013)

The Royal Disease
Haemophilia and the Romanovs

Queen Victoria was a carrier of haemophilia B. It is likely that she developed the abnormal gene by spontaneous mutation. Haemophilia B was first reported in a patient named Stephen Christmas in 1952, in the Christmas edition of the *British Medical Journal*. It is an X-linked recessive disorder.

Victoria had nine children by Albert. One son, Leopold, had haemophilia, which was not publicly admitted. Two daughters, Alice and Beatrice were carriers. Alice's daughter, Alexandra, married the future Czar Nicholas II. Their only son, Alexei, manifest the disease. Beatrice's daughter, Eugene, married the future King Alfonso XII of Spain and their first son had haemophilia. The Czarevich Alexei's haemophilia became central to many events in Russia in the short 13 years of his life. One can reasonably speculate would Russian history have taken a different course had he not suffered from the disease.

Haemophilia B is an X-linked recessive disorder caused by deficiency of factor IX. It comprises approximately 20% of the total population of haemophiliacs. The son of a carrier mother has a 50% chance of manifesting the disease and her daughter a 50% chance of becoming a silent carrier. It may also arise de novo, as a result of spontaneous gene mutation. Such mutations may account for up to 30% of all cases.

The gene encoding factor IX is located near the end of the long arm of the X chromosome and is the largest gene of its family. A genotype analysis carried out on bone specimens from the remains of the murdered Romanov family showed the mutation occurred in F9, leading to the production of a truncated form of factor IX.

Alexandra (Alix/Sunny) was the daughter of Duke Ludwig of Hesse and Princess Alice, daughter of Victoria. Alice was subject to depression. Alice and her youngest daughter died of diphtheria when Alix was six. Her brother, Frederick (Frittie) had haemophilia from which he died after a fall from a window. Victoria acted from a distance as a surrogate mother, ensuring that Alix was tutored by an English governess. She was vulnerable, neurotic and rarely smiled yet, had an iron will.

She first met Nicholas at her sister's wedding when she was 11 years old. She was not impressed but he was. Five years later, they met again and started corresponding but, Victoria wanted her to marry Prince Eddie, heir to the British crown. Nicky's parents, Czar Alexander III and Minnie wanted him to marry Helene, the daughter of the Comte de Paris. Alix was a fervent Lutheran and if she married into the Romanov family, would be expected to convert to Russian Orthodox. Though Nicky had by now started a long affair with a Polish ballerina (Little K) he wrote in his diary, "I never stop thinking of Alix."

When they met again, at another family wedding in Coburg, he asked her again if she would change religion. She said no. Kaiser Willie took her aside for a talk. Next day, she told Nicky she would convert. They got engaged but Victoria kept her in Windsor to study Russian. Not long after, she was called to St Petersburg as Nicky's father was dying. The critically ill Emperor insisted on greeting Alix in full regalia and expressed the wish that the marriage proceed as soon as possible.

After his death, Alix was received into the Orthodox church and a month later, they were married. In November 1895, she delivered a healthy baby girl, Olga. She had three more daughters in the following years: Tatiana Maria and Anastasia.

A month after she had Anastasia, she met a French healer, Philippe and became infatuated with his spiritism. Desperate to have an heir, Phillipe advised bathing in the spring of St Seraphim. Soon after, she was pregnant again and all Russia wished it to be a boy. A 301-gun salute confirmed the birth of an heir.

Alix, familiar with haemophilia as her brother had the disease, was concerned that the baby bled from the navel for two days after the birth and again at six weeks. Her worst fears were now realised. They decided to keep the diagnosis a secret, to protect the Romanov brand. Only close family ever knew the diagnosis for certain. Another burden was now added to the neurotic, overstressed mother. She was determined however, that little Alexei would succeed his father in due course.

Philippe had died when Rasputin first met the royal couple. They were very taken by his hypnotic gaze and his apparent spirituality. He prayed over Alexei, who was two years old and having a minor bleed. Long term, Rasputin came to symbolise the weakness and dependency of Nicky and Alix. He became a hated political player but only because they allowed it.

Grigori Rasputin was born in Pokrovskoye, in the Tobolsk region of Siberia. Not a serf (they were none in Siberia), he was illiterate. Leaving his wife and children, he spent time in a monastery learning to read and write. He became a pilgrim or *stranik*. He never formally took holy orders but, became known to his followers as a *starets* or elder.

Aged three, Alexei had a severe bleed. His doctors were very pessimistic and in desperation, Alix asked Rasputin to pray over the child, who immediately improved. He began to visit the palace regularly and the upper classes in Petersburg were appalled. Alix and her daughters frequently wrote to him. An Orthodox priest stole a cache of letters and showed them to a politician, who gave them to Nicky. The press started a campaign against him. He was forced to leave Petersburg and return home to Siberia.

In September 1912, the eight-year-old Alexei injured himself on a family hunting expedition in Spala, Poland. He had major bleeding. A week later, his doctors gave up hope and he received the last rites. Alix, frantic with worry, telegraphed Rasputin in Siberia. He telegraphed back, "The little one will not die" and advised that she should not let his doctors bother the child too much. This might well have helped, as doctors gave aspirin for pain which would have aggravated the bleeding. The child's fever abated and bleeding stopped within 24 hours.

Alix was now convinced that Rasputin was indispensable. Police protection was put in place but in 1914, on a visit home, he was attacked by a woman with a knife. A gaping wound in the abdomen revealed his entrails. The Czar dispatched his personal doctor and Rasputin survived, taking two months to recover. A church plot was suspected but the woman insisted she had acted alone.

War clouds gathered and Russia got drawn into the conflict that became World War I, in defence of Serbia. The war effort did not go well and Nicholas decided (unwisely) in 1915, to himself assume supreme command of the Russian forces. Now physically well removed from Petersburg, by default, he virtually handed over the running of the country to Alix. In turn, she increasingly sought Rasputin's advice on political appointments. Rasputin consistently opposed the war.

Alexei, aged 11, joined his father in military HQ. The boy, so cosseted, delighted in wearing military uniform and shared a bedroom with his father. The Russian armies now achieved some success in the field. On the home front however, things went from bad to worse. People queued for food and inflation raged. One incompetent after another was appointed or fired by Alix, who was increasingly relying on Rasputin's advice.

Rasputin was now drinking heavily and openly consorting with prostitutes. He was also boasting of his influence on the Romanovs. Felix Yusipov and Dmitri Pavlovich conspired, with others including members of the British embassy, to kill him in order to save the dynasty. It was known that Rasputin opposed the war and the British were anxious to keep Russia fighting.

In December 1916, Yusipov tricked him into coming to his palace, late one night, on the false story that his wife, Irena, would be there. Cream cakes sprinkled with cyanide were prepared but it is not certain Rasputin ate them as expected. When the poison appeared not to be working, Yusipov shot him through the lower chest, the bullet passing through the liver. Rasputin collapsed and Yusipov went to fetch his accomplices to move the body. When he returned to the scene, Rasputin suddenly lunged at him and then climbed the stairs into a courtyard. A co-conspirator, Puriskevich, fired four shots hitting him with two. Rasputin fell, in the snow. He then received the *coup de gras*, almost certainly from Rayner of the British Embassy. They disposed of the body in an ice hole, in the little Neva river but failed to weight it down. It was located by police after 48 hours. His killers were exiled without trial.

Many close family members now implored Nicholas to remove his wife from her political role. Rasputin's killing would have given him a good excuse. All previous mistakes could have been blamed on Rasputin's bad advice. He refused. She was highly indignant at the suggestion that her actions were leading to an implosion of the dynasty. There were numerous strikes and riots in St Petersburg, now renamed Petrograd.

Nicholas finally decided to return from army HQ on 1 March 1917. By then, law and order had completely broken down in the capital. His train was blocked by insurgents, so it reversed and took a circuitous route. For 15 hours, he was incommunicado. Parliament fell and a delegation set out to secure his abdication. When his train next stopped for lunch, he was informed that the army generals, all monarchists, had voted unanimously in favour of abdication. As the army was the bedrock of the dynasty Nicholas agreed to abdicate in favour of Alexei, appointing his brother Michael as regent. After a discussion with the court physician about the long-term health prospects of Alexei, Nicholas changed the terms abdicating "in my name and his." Michael, who never wanted the position, was now proclaimed Czar. Michael abdicated after one day.

Back in the family palace, Tsarskoe Selo, Nicky, now Colonel Romanov, was under house arrest. The foreign minister suggested the family be sent into exile in England. George V had offered this but was increasingly uneasy, fearing it might destabilise the position of the English royal family. Against the wishes of Lloyd George, he asked that the Russians be informed that the British Royals must be allowed to withdraw the offer of asylum.

As all the Romanov girls came down with measles at the time, it might not have been possible to evacuate the family. Kerensky, the interim prime minister, decided the family needed to be moved, for their own safety, from the environs of Petrograd. After a five-day journey, they arrived in Tobolsk. They were treated with kindness while detained there. The four princesses even struck up friendships with some of the guards.

The Bolsheviks seized power in October and Kerensky was ousted. Lenin wanted to bring the Czar to the new capital, Moscow and put him on trial. Trotsky was to act as prosecutor. Perhaps fearing that sympathetic elements might free him on the journey, Lenin decided instead to move the family further east to Ekaterinburg.

Alexei had suffered a severe bleed following an accident on the stairs. Even the unsympathetic Bolshevik commander saw that he was too ill to travel so, Nicky and Alix went first, followed by the children a month later.

Two months later, the family were awakened at 1.30am and told to dress, as they were being moved again due to unrest in the region. The local Soviet leader, Yurovsky, had cleared their killing with Lenin. Nicholas carried Alexei down to the basement room. He sat him on a chair then stood in front of him. Yurovsky then read out the death sentence. He drew his pistol and shot Nicholas.

Though the firing squad had been allocated a specific family member to shoot, they all discharged their weapons at Nicholas. Chaos ensued. Alexei was still sitting, his shirt spattered with his father's blood. Yurovsky and his deputy shot the 13-year-old in the chest and he fell, moaning, to the ground. Another killer, Ermakov, tried to finish off the boy, stabbing him repeatedly in the chest with a bayonet. Still alive Yurovsky shot him in the head at close range.

It took ten minutes before all were dead. Lenin announced that the Czar had been executed and the family evacuated. It was not until the fall of the Soviet Union that the bodies were finally recovered.

The last Czarevich of Russia suffered from haemophilia B, inherited through his mother from Queen Victoria. That particular mutation now appears to be extinct. His parents, Nicholas and Alexandra, decided to keep his illness a secret.

Rasputin appeared uniquely capable of controlling some of the worst bleeds. Rasputin was not only able to calm Alexei down but, as important, could do the same with the highly-strung Alexandra. It is speculated that Rasputin was brought in at a time when the attacks were coming to a close in any case. No one can explain how Rasputin appeared able to influence a particularly severe attack of bleeding while thousands of miles away in Siberia. This particular episode, where the royal doctors had given up hope, convinced Alexandra that Rasputin's presence in Petersburg was indispensable. When Nicholas left for the Russian HQ, having installed himself as commander-in-chief of the forces, he left Alexandra in charge of domestic affairs. This proved disastrous, as she came to rely on Rasputin.

When Nicholas abdicated, there was a short window of opportunity when the family might have been saved by going into exile in England. George V, however, withdrew his offer of sanctuary. Any hope they had of being allowed to leave Russia vanished when the Bolsheviks seized power.

Further Reading

"Genotype Analysis Identifies the Cause of the 'Royal Disease'" by E.I. Rogaev et al in *Science* (2009), 326:5954 p817

"The History of Haemophilia in the Royal Families of Europe" by R. Stevens in *British Journal of Haematology* (1999) 105 25-32

The Romanovs by Simon Sebag Montefiore (Weidenfeld and Nicolson, London. 2016)

Alexander Fleming

The Man and the Myth

"When I woke up just before dawn on September 28th, 1928, I didn't plan to revolutionise all medicine by discovering the world's first antibiotic – but I suppose that is exactly what I did." – **Alexander Fleming**

"Chance favours only the prepared mind." – **Louis Pasteur**

The author has good reason to be grateful to the antibiotic, Penicillin. At the age of 13 years, I suffered from a burst appendix with a pelvic abscess. Following surgery, I had several weeks of intensive hospital care including twice daily injections of a Penicillin Streptomycin combination. Procaine had not yet been combined with Penicillin, so the injections were intensely painful. I had a rubber pelvic drain in place for 10 days. My total recovery period was three months. I have little doubt that, without antibiotics, I would have died from sepsis.

As every schoolboy knew, Alexander Fleming had discovered Penicillin. I felt I owed my life to that Scottish pioneer. Much later, as a medical student, I learned the full story of how Penicillin was developed, refined and produced in vast quantities, playing a huge medical role in World War II.

It was Florey, Chain and Heatley in Oxford who did the hard bit. They purified, manufactured it and did the first trials on animals and humans. Initially, only small amounts were harvested. Later with the cooperation of Richards in the USA, they developed techniques allowing significant quantities to be manufactured. While Fleming discovered it in 1928, he did not think it was likely to be useful in controlling infection in vivo. He failed to interest any biochemist in researching it further and finally abandoned his work on it.

Alexander Fleming was born in Ayrshire in Scotland in 1881. He was the third of four children of farmer, Hugh Fleming and his second wife, Grace Stirling Morton. There were also four surviving children of Hugh's first marriage. His father died when he was seven years old.

After early schooling in Scotland, he completed his undergraduate time in the Royal Polytechnic Institute in London. He qualified MBBS in St Mary's Paddington in 1906. The captain of the rifle club in St Mary's wished to retain him on his team, as he was a good shot and suggested he join the Bacteriology Department in the hospital. He did so and took a BSc degree, majoring in Bacteriology. He served as a Captain in the RAMC during the First World War. Post war, he returned to St Mary's and was appointed Professor of Bacteriology in 1928.

He discovered the enzyme, Lysozyme, when working on nasal secretions, finding it had an inhibitory effect against many harmless bacteria. Later, while working on Staphylococci, he returned from a month's vacation and found one of the cultures contaminated with mould. He noticed the Staphylococcal colonies adjacent to the mould were suppressed. He grew the mould and identified it as of the Penicillium genus. He named it Penicillin.

He found penicillin inhibited the growth of Gram-positive pathogens and one Gram-negative organism, Neisseria gonorrhoeae in vitro. He published his discovery in the *British Journal of Experimental Pathology*. There was little or no reaction to the article.

He continued to grow the mould but found it difficult to isolate the antibiotic element. He concluded it was unlikely to be effective in vivo. He continued to try and interest chemists with the skills to refine it but finally abandoned work on it. About this time, Florey and Chain in Oxford independently began studies on antibacterial substances, including penicillin. Chain and Abraham discovered how to isolate and concentrate it while Abraham worked out its structure. When the Oxford team published their initial paper, Fleming telephoned Florey. When Florey told Chain of the call, Chain said, "good God I thought he was dead!"

Florey and Chain

Howard Walter Florey was an Australian pathologist and Ernst Boris Chain, a German biochemist. Temperamentally they were unlikely co-workers. Florey was quick tempered and Chain had a particularly prickly personality.

Florey qualified in Adelaide. He obtained a Rhodes Scholarship to Oxford, not only due to academic ability but also being a fine tennis player. He later became a Rockefeller Foundation Fellow, enabling him to work with Alfred Newton Richards, a pharmacologist in Pennsylvania. This partnership was to prove a vital one later, when he needed technical support in the USA to mass produce penicillin. After his time in Pennsylvania, he completed a PhD in Cambridge, becoming Director of the Dunne School of Pathology in Oxford, in 1936. By 1940, he had assembled a team of scientists and technicians to work on penicillin.

Ernst Boris Chain was born in Berlin in 1906. He took a chemistry and physiology degree in 1930. Being Jewish, he felt unsafe in Germany with the rise of Hitler and left for England in 1933. Sadly, his mother and sister who remained in Germany perished in the Holocaust. In 1939, he became a British subject and that year, joined Florey's team in Oxford. An exceptionally gifted pianist, he contemplated a career as a concert pianist but decided to pursue a career in science. With Abraham, he identified a technique for purifying and concentrating penicillin.

Another member of the team, Norman Heatley, made significant improvements in the concentration process. Even then, the amounts produced were tiny but sufficient to trial in animals.

Eight mice were injected with haemolytic streptococci. The four who received penicillin survived. All four control mice died. The results were published in the *Lancet*, in 1940.

The first human patient to be treated was a policeman, Albert Alexander, who developed septicaemia following a scratch from a rose thorn. He made an initial recovery but, despite harvesting penicillin from his urine, the entire supply ran out and he died a month later. Florey determined to somehow have a sufficient supply in the future.

The first successful cure was in 1942, when Anne Muller in New Haven, Connecticut survived sepsis post miscarriage when treated with penicillin.

Surface culture was used initially and became increasingly difficult to accommodate physically in Oxford. More staff were hired. As production increased, Chain suggested taking out a patent, as was the norm in Germany. Florey refused, to the great irritation of Chain, on the basis that the drug would benefit all mankind. (Paradoxically, when he discovered Cephalosporin C in 1954, Florey immediately applied for a patent).

Attempts to interest pharmaceutical companies in England to produce penicillin were largely unsuccessful, as these firms were already at full stretch supplying the war effort. It was decided to explore the possibility of getting assistance from the USA, which was still a non-combatant. Florey and Heatley flew to the USA, where large scale fermentation processes were being studied by the US Department of Agriculture in Peoria, Illinois.

Fortuitously, Florey's former director from his time as a Rockefeller Fellow in Pennsylvania, A.N. Richards, had become chair of the Scientific Research Committee set up to strengthen Allied resources. Richards was quickly convinced by Florey of the importance of pushing ahead with a joint programme, aimed at mass producing penicillin. Florey and Heatley were aware that the mould, penicillium notatum, was unlikely to produce sufficient penicillin for mass use. Serendipitously they discovered penicillium crysogeum, which yielded 100 times more and after x-ray filtration, 1000 times more than Notatum.

While Florey returned to England, Heatley stayed on in the US, working with Andrew Moyer. They successfully modified and optimised the growth medium. Heatley found Moyer becoming more secretive but only discovered the reason in 1942, when Moyer published the work under his own name and applied for a patent on the technique.

Nobel Prize

In 1945, Fleming, Florey and Chain shared the Nobel Prize in Physiology or Medicine. Nobel Prize rules state that a maximum of three can share a prize in any of the award disciplines. Posthumous awards are also prohibited. Heatley should certainly have been recognised and it would have been within the gift of the Prize Committee to award him one in a different category. Oxford University tried to make some recompense by awarding him an Honorary Doctorate in Medicine. This was the first such doctorate awarded to a non-medically qualified recipient in the 800-year history of that university.

Irish Connections

Alexander Fleming's first wife was Sarah Marion McElroy, a nurse born in Killala, Co. Mayo.

Ernst Chain loved Mayo, taking his family on vacation there many times. He ultimately built a retirement home in Mulranny and lived there for nine years. He died in Castlebar Hospital in 1979. There is a road named in commemoration of him in Castlebar.

The late Dr Madeline O Connell was a Cork graduate who worked for Fleming. When asked if she was intimidated working for such a famous man she replied, "Not at all."

Indeed, knowing Madeline, it may well be that she intimidated him – in the nicest possible way!

Conclusions

Fleming was lionised when Britain needed heroes, late in World War II. An affable man, unlike Florey, he was quite happy to talk to the press. While remaining personally modest, he did nothing to dispel what he himself called the "Fleming myth". He did praise Florey and Chain for transforming Penicillin into a practical drug. In the last decade of his life, he was Knighted and received multiple other honours, including many Honorary Degrees. He had audiences with Pope Pius XII and became a member of the Pontifical Academy of Sciences.

While he did recognise that he had stumbled on an interesting discovery in 1928, it was not he who put Penicillin to the test. It was Florey, Chain and Heatley who did the difficult part and established its value as an antibiotic. In addition, with the help of their American colleagues, they established the techniques by which it was mass produced. To some extent then, Fleming was happy to go along with the myth that he deserved the major credit for discovering the wonder drug, Penicillin. Initially the Oxford group were astounded at the press adulation of Fleming, with little or no credit given to their contribution. To some extent, the joint Nobel Prize redressed matters though, sadly not for Heatley.

In the final analysis, however, as Sir Henry Harris put it, "Without Fleming, no Chain or Florey, without Florey no Heatley: without Heatley no Penicillin."

Further Reading

Alexander Fleming: The Man and the Myth by Gwyn MacFarlane (Hogarth Press [Chatto & Windus], London. 1984)

Stalin's Death and The Doctors' Plot
Cheyne-Stokes Breathing and an Uncle's Legacy

John Cheyne and William Stokes would be astounded to hear that the characteristic breathing pattern they described individually, which bears their joint names, would feature in such an odd way in Stalin's death. Stalin had stated at a banquet, celebrating victory over the Nazis in 1945, that he would work another two or three years and then, "I will have to retire."

His marshals unanimously told him that he had many years of ruling ahead of him and, suggested promoting him to the title Generalissimo, which he accepted with a show of reluctance. However, already suffering from atherosclerosis, he had a number of minor strokes and probable heart attacks in the following years. Despite this, his political power was undiminished. Possible successors remained fearful for their survival and his mood swings, intrigues and paranoia left no-one feeling secure. Indeed, he continued to order the killing of associates, marking the lists with symbols specifying how they were supposed to die.

The last major show trial planned, "The Doctors' Plot", had its genesis in 1950. That year, Dr Yakov Etinger, who was being bugged, was found to be discussing the health of his patient, Stalin, too frankly. Despite incriminating his fellow Jewish doctors in Moscow, Etinger was tortured to death.

Cheyne-Stokes Breathing
John Cheyne, in 1818, described a patient with a terminal stroke who had a peculiar breathing pattern over a period of 8 or 9 days. Breathing would cease for 15 seconds and then resume, becoming rapid and deep before ceasing temporarily again.

William Stokes described a similar pattern, independently, in 1846. He described a patient with very faint breathing periods followed by heaving and violent breaths. Breathing was then suspended for 15 seconds "so that his attendants were frequently in doubt whether he was not actually dead."

Risk factors for Cheyne-Stokes Breathing included male gender, advanced age, atrial fibrillation and hypocapnia. The respiratory control centre in the brain initiates apnoea when carbon dioxide (CO_2) falls below the "Apnoeic Threshold". This is, in part, due to loss of sensitivity of the mid brain to hypoxia. Delayed circulation time prolongs a period between the rise in CO_2 and its detection by the respiratory control centre. Hypercapnia ensues by the time the centre ends the period of apnoea, leading to a repeat of the breathing sequence.

Background to the Doctors' Plot

Andrei Zhdanov, already in poor health due to heart disease and alcoholism, was considered a likely successor to Stalin in 1946. In 1947, he enthusiastically supported the tightening of control over the New Eastern Europe empire and later created the new Communist International – the Cominform – to strengthen these ties. He encountered unexpected resistance to the Cominform from Tito, who refused to be overawed by Stalin.

Already a sick man, Zhdanov had a further heart attack and a minor stroke. He was sent to a sanatorium for treatment and was visited there by Vinogradov, Stalin's personal physician. Inexplicably, the local team of doctors prescribed exercise. A row broke out when Dr Lydia Timashuk diagnosed myocardial infarction based on electrocardiography. She was pressurised into revising the diagnosis and to rewrite her report in vaguer terms. Zhdanov had a further heart attack and died in 1948. By now, Timashuk (a covert secret service agent) had written a letter of denunciation of her colleagues' mismanagement of the case and had given it to General Vlasic, to deliver personally to Stalin. We know Stalin received and initialled it however, nothing was done. Timashuk was fired from her position.

Throughout 1950, Stalin kept the anti-Semitic pot simmering. This hatred was also fuelled by his perception that his beloved daughter, Svetlana, seemed to be especially attracted to Jewish men. Late that year, Professor Yakov Etinger was arrested, having been bugged while discussing Stalin's health. Under torture, he incriminated a large number of Jewish doctors. His torturer, Ryumin, was too enthusiastic however and Etinger died.

By now Stalin's health was failing. He had a series of transient ischemic attacks (TIA's). By 1952, his guards had installed phones on the routes of his walks, in case he needed to call for help. His personal physician, Vinogradov advised complete rest. Stalin was furious and ordered that that medical record be destroyed. Vinogradov now found himself a suspect. (He was finally arrested in November of that year).

In the spring, a large cohort of doctors were arrested and tortured, followed by another group in September. To make it as anti-Semitic as possible, instructions were that the bulk of doctors arrested were to be Jewish. A case was now being prepared against the doctors, who had supposedly killed their patients by inappropriate management. Conveniently, the filed denunciation by Timashuk in 1948 was resurrected. Was this evidence of the supposed "Deliberate killing of Zhdanov"? *Pravda* announced the doctor's arrest with the chilling headline, "Vicious Spies and Killers behind the Mask of Academic Physicians."

Stalin's Death

On the fateful night of 28 February 1953, Stalin discussed progress in the Doctors' Plot. Assured that confessions were imminent, he stressed that they needed to be impressive. If not, he threatened that the chief interrogator, Ignatiev, "would be shortened by a head."

Beria assured him, "They will confess."

He held a final dinner party in the company of Beria, Khrushchev, Malenkov and Bulganin at his Dacha in Kuntsevo, ending at 4am the following morning. Announcing that he was going to bed, he instructed his guards that he was not to be disturbed. The guards got anxious when he had not called for his usual cup of tea next morning but, were relieved when, at 6pm, they saw lights switched on in his rooms.

Apprehension rose as hours went by without a summons. Lozgachev, one of the personal guards, finally decided to enter his quarters at 10pm, to deliver a batch of official papers. Stalin was lying on the floor in a pool of urine. He was conscious but, unable to speak. Lozgachev called two other attendants and they lifted him onto the sofa. No one felt empowered to call a doctor so, they rang the Secret Service boss, Ignatiev. He was too frightened to take the initiative of calling for medical assistance but, instructed the guard to phone Beria and Malenkov. Beria instructed him to keep complete secrecy about Stalin's illness.

In the small hours of 2 March, Malenkov and Beria arrived at the dacha. Stalin was snoring. When the guards asked permission to call a doctor, Beria told them not to cause unnecessary panic as, "Obviously the boss is sleeping peacefully."

The guards, fearful that they would be blamed if he died, again asked if medical aid could be sought. Finally, some twelve hours after the probable onset of his stroke, the Minister of Health was phoned by Beria and Malenkov, and asked to send some Russian, non-Jewish doctors. As all the first line doctors who were familiar with his health problems were locked up in Lubyanka Prison, a completely new team were summoned.

Contemporary reports indicate that this group were terrified. Leaches (*Hirud medicinalis*) were applied behind his ears and he was injected with camphor (a stimulant introduced by Arab medicine). As the day progressed, more leaches were applied.

New doctors were called in. By 4 March, his breathing had developed into the Cheyne-Stokes pattern.

Their interrogator summoned three of the imprisoned doctors. To their surprise, they were asked by their interrogator to comment on the significance of a medical diagnosis he had received in the case of "my uncle, who has Cheyne-Stokes breathing."

The baffled doctors replied along the lines, "If you are expecting an inheritance from your uncle, you won't have to wait long."

By 5 March, Stalin's breathing had become shallower and at noon, he vomited blood. About 10pm, he was injected with camphor and adrenaline but, died soon after. In all probability it would have made little difference if medical aid had been sought earlier. However, his henchmen (all under suspicion by him, for one reason or another) were happy to stand by and let him die. Robert Service, in his biography of Stalin, recounts that opponents solemnly toasted the health of the American doctor (sic) Cheyne Stokes on each anniversary of Stalin's death!

Pravda suddenly stopped its attacks on doctors on 2 March 1953 though, other publications continued them. Some historians now claim that Stalin had decided to abandon the Doctors Plot. This seems unlikely as, he appeared fully committed to it just before his final illness.

The collective leadership that followed his death dismissed the charges against the doctors, who were exonerated by 31 March of that year. Ryumin, whose over-enthusiastic torture had killed Etinger, was accused of fabricating the plot. He was arrested an executed. Timashuk, whose letter of condemnation in 1948 had been used to bolster the accusation, had her Order of Lenin award revoked.

Epilogue
Had Stalin lived, the doctors would have been exposed to a show trial. This was designed to be as much an anti-Semitic event as an

anti-doctor one. Stalin had already sent instructions to the trial judge to "beat them, beat them and beat them again" if they did not confess. Indeed, Stalin had already decided that the doctors would be executed by firing squad. His death, paradoxically, saved them from certain execution.

Further Reading

Irish Masters of Medicine by Davis Coakley (Town House, Dublin. 1992)

Stalin: The Court of the Red Tsar by Simon Sebag Montefiore (Weidenfeld and Nicolson, London. 2003)

Stalin: A Biography by Robert Service (Pan Books, London. 2010)

Russia by Martin Sixsmith (BBC Books, London. 2011)

Rosalind Franklin

Her Role in the Discovery of the Double Helix

When I attended the Brussels Expo in 1958, the central motif was a molecular structure, *The Atomium*. While the highlight for me was to see "Sputnik" in the Russian Pavilion, there was a molecular structure displayed in the British Pavilion. This was a model of the Tobacco Mosaic Virus by a British scientist I had never heard of – Rosalind Franklin.

Rosalind Franklin was born into an Ashkenazi Jewish family in Notting Hill, London. She attended St Paul's Girls' School, where she first demonstrated her ability in Science. She studied Chemistry in Newnham College, Cambridge in 1938, with parental encouragement. Awarded a second-class honours in her final exams in 1941, she took on wartime work with the British Coal Board. This work formed the basis of a Ph.D. thesis, awarded by Cambridge University.

Keen to expand her practical knowledge of physical chemistry, she secured a post with Jacques Mering in Paris. In his laboratory, she learned X-ray Crystallography. She spent four productive and happy years in Paris. For family reasons, she returned to London where she took up a three-year fellowship in the Medical Research Council's Biophysics Unit in Kings. It seems clear that the Director, John Randall, asked her to take over DNA X-ray Diffraction work. Maurice Wilkins had been doing this work and understood Franklin was coming as his assistant. This was a major factor in the personal friction which developed between Franklin and Wilkins. Randall tried to resolve the clash by dividing the work on DNA, Franklin choosing to work with the A and Wilkins the B form.

Franklin had a blunt, direct personality, very different from Wilkins. The poor communication between them was not helped by the fact that, while all the MRC staff lunched together, women were not allowed upstairs for afternoon coffee in the smoking room. This contrasted profoundly with the egalitarian regime she was used to in Paris. Indeed, she became so profoundly unhappy in Kings that, despite the great scientific breakthroughs in her work, she applied to leave a year early, transferring her fellowship to Birkbeck College.

She was recruited to Birkbeck by the Irish scientist, J.D. Bernal, who had also taught Wilkins in Cambridge. As part of his agreement to allow her transfer, Randall made it a condition that she did not pursue further work on DNA. Additionally, all her diffraction photographs and work on DNA structure were to be left with Wilkins. Though she did much further fundamental research, especially on the Tobacco Mosaic Virus, it is for her contributions to the structure of DNA during the Kings years for which she is best remembered. Tragically she developed ovarian cancer, from which she died in April 1958 aged 37 years.

In 1953, Watson and Crick published their theoretical model of the double helical structure of DNA in the journal, *Nature*, acknowledging, in a footnote, that their work had been stimulated by a general knowledge of Franklin and Wilkins unpublished data. In the same issue, articles by Wilkins and Franklin were published second and third, appearing only to support the Watson and Crick theoretical paper. By that time, Franklin had transferred to Birkbeck College. When Watson, Crick and Wilkins received the Nobel Prize in Medicine in 1962, Franklin was deceased and could not have been nominated under the rules of the Committee.

Controversy

Watson published his book, *The Double Helix*, in 1968 and it became a best-seller. Racily written, it is a great read and a new, annotated and illustrated version has recently been published. In their Nobel Prize acceptance speeches, Watson and Crick failed to mention the contribution Franklin's work had made to their theoretical model, indeed neither of them mentioned her name at all. It was left to Wilkins to make a minor reference to her.

In *The Double Helix*, Watson portrayed Franklin as a belligerent woman, unable to keep her emotions under control. He further commented – "Clearly Rosie had to go or be put in her place."

This caused great distress to her family; indeed, it appears that Rosie was a name never used by herself, her colleagues or friends. In a presentation attended by Watson in 1951, she had described two forms of the DNA molecule with the sugar-phosphate units located externally. Watson later claimed not to have understood her talk or taken notes. Later, Wilkins showed an X-ray photograph of B DNA (historically known as photograph 51) to Watson, almost certainly without her knowledge, early in 1953. An internal report of an MRC visit to Kings in December 1952, which included some of Franklin's X-ray data, was also shown by Max Perutz to Crick, "since it had not been marked as confidential."

The fact was first revealed when *The Double Helix* was published and led to Perutz having to explain why he had shown an internal report. He claimed inexperience in administrative matters. As Franklin was deceased when *The Double Helix* was published, she was not protected by libel laws.

Rosalind Franklin was a gifted scientist with a difficult and sometimes abrasive personality. Similar abrasiveness might well have been excused if she had been a man in Britain in the early 1950s. A mutual antipathy between Franklin and Wilkins was most unfortunate. It seems clear that Wilkins was keen to collaborate with Watson and Crick in Cambridge. Indeed, the day after Watson and Crick had finished their model, on 7th March 1953, they got a letter from Wilkins saying that as Franklin was finally leaving, they could "put all hands to the pump."

Rosalind's sister, Jenifer Glynn, has written a moving and sensitive account of her sister's life. ("Remembering my sister, Rosalind Franklin" – *Lancet*, 24 March 2012.) Posthumous recognition has been striking and is, hopefully, providing some solace to her family. Such recognition has included Finch University in Chicago changing its name to the Rosalind Franklin University of Medicine and Science. One can only echo the statement of Elkin (*Physics Today*, 2013) that "There was enough glory in the work of the four to be shared by them all."

However, to this day, Watson still maintains that Franklin was unable to interpret her own DNA data.

Anthony Eden and the Suez Crisis

The Role of Illness in his Flawed Decision Making

Anthony Eden was Prime Minister in waiting for several decades in the UK. He appeared the ideal candidate to succeed Churchill. He was awarded the Military Cross (MC) in World War I. Most of his ministerial career was spent in the Foreign Office. In 1939, he resigned his post as Foreign Secretary, in protest at Chamberlain's appeasement policy towards Mussolini's expansionist policies in the Mediterranean. Always a bit of a dandy he was a member of the POP club in Eton, being allowed to wear a coloured waistcoat. He was noted as a smart dresser and his trademark was a Homburg hat. Mussolini hit back, mocking him as "the best dressed fool in Europe."

His negotiating skills were highly admired. In World War II, he was a restraining hand on the impulsive Churchill. When Labour won the 1945 general election, many thought Churchill would retire and make Eden party leader. It is suggested that Eden did ask Churchill (who already had a minor stroke in 1949) to cede him power. Instead, he made Eden deputy leader of the Conservative party. He was, however, de facto leader as Churchill had so many other commitments.

When Churchill won the 1951 election, he took on the Prime Minister role again, appointing Eden to Foreign Secretary. He asked the King to appoint Eden deputy Prime Minister but, the request was refused for lack of precedent. It is suggested that the King encouraged Churchill to hand over the premiership in 1951 but, he declined to do so.

In 1953, Eden had surgery for gallstones, which was botched. Soon after, Churchill had a major stroke but, this illness was covered up by compliant press barons and not revealed to the British public. Finally, in 1955, Churchill handed over to Eden, who called a general election. Immensely popular, Eden increased the Conservative majority from 17 to 58.

While Eden was considered a bit out of touch with domestic politics, it is ironic that his premiership collapsed due to a spectacular disaster of foreign policy – an area in which he was vastly experienced. There is much to suggest that his botched biliary surgery, consequent cholangitis and his use of prescribed "uppers" and "downers" adversely affected his judgment in the Suez Crisis.

Biliary Tract Surgery

Eden was diagnosed with a duodenal ulcer in 1945 by Lord Moran (nicknamed "Corkscrew Charlie" by the medical profession for his machinations in the introduction of the National Health Service). In 1952, he had several bouts of severe upper-abdominal pain, one accompanied by jaundice. In April 1953, he had further severe pain and x-rays showed gallstones. The Queen's physician, Sir Horace Evans, was consulted and advised cholecystectomy. He gave Eden the names of three surgeons who specialised in gallbladder surgery. Eden decided to go to Mr John Basil Hume, a general surgeon who had removed his appendix in his youth. There was no reason to believe the operation would be anything but routine.

On 12 April 1953, Hume operated, assisted by Mr Guy Blackburn. No one is sure of what went wrong. Sir Christopher Booth opined that the common bile duct was ligated in error. Certainly, the bile duct was damaged. The right branch of the hepatic artery was almost certainly injured and, possibly ligated. Richard Thorpe has written that Hume became so agitated, the operation was put on hold for an hour. Eden was told that the surgeon's knife had slipped, cutting the duct inadvertently. On 29 April, Mr Blackburn re-operated, evacuating a collection of bile. He may also have attempted to repair the bile duct unsuccessfully.

Dr Richard Cattell, an internationally respected expert on complex biliary surgery, happened to be in London and was invited to give his opinion. He strongly advised further surgery, which he offered to carry out in his own base, the Lahey Clinic in Boston. Churchill, probably egged on by Moran, initially insisted further surgery should be done in London. Evans and Cattell had to visit him in No 10 Downing Street to persuade him that the surgery should be done in Boston.

On 10 June, Cattell found a biliary duodenal fistula, which he repaired. A very short section of the common hepatic duct was identified. The right and left hepatic ducts were probed and were patent. A segment of upper small bowel was attached to the liver and a Y-tube was put in place as a stent.

Recovery was uneventful and, he remained well until 1954, when he had fever and chills typical of biliary infection (cholangitis). Three bouts of cholangitis occurred in 1955. On 5 October, while visiting his wife in University College Hospital, he had a severe attack of cholangitis, his temperature rising to 106° F. A room was found for him and he was discharged on 8 October. He was now on antibiotics, sedatives to help him sleep and amphetamines to elevate his mood. During this time, the Suez Crisis was coming to a head. Not surprisingly, he was described as agitated, jumpy and nervy at meetings.

Suez Crisis

In June 1956, the last British troops left Port Said in Egypt, under the terms of a bilateral agreement negotiated, paradoxically, by Eden when he was Foreign Secretary. Gamal Abdel Nasser, the Egyptian president who had overthrown King Farouk, announced to a wildly enthusiastic crowd in Alexandria, on 26 July, that he was nationalising the Suez Canal. He promised not to interfere with international use of the canal but, pledged to use the income from running it towards the building of the Aswan High Dam.

The USA and Britain had initially offered to fund the High Dam at Aswan. The offer was withdrawn due to deals Nassar did with the USSR and Czechoslovakia and especially, as he gave diplomatic recognition to China. John Foster Dulles (nicknamed 'Dull, Duller, Dulles'), the American Secretary of State, was convinced that the USSR would not fund the project. He was wrong.

Nasser fomented riots in Amman, which led to the sacking of Glubb Pasha and all other British officers in Jordan, in March 1956. King Hussein feared that his throne was under threat but, assured Britain privately that the Hashemite dynasty remained an ally.

On 27 July, Eden had a long session with a senior cabinet ministers and the Chiefs of Staff. Thomas, the Sea Lord, felt military action should not be delayed but, Eden was cautious. Eisenhower, running for re-election, made it clear that public opinion in the USA would not back a military attack on Egypt over the nationalisation of the canal. However, oil reserves in Britain were down to six weeks and, it was heavily reliant on supplies transported via the canal.

Eden, already sick and sleep deprived, developed an implacable hatred of Nasser, who he now equated to Mussolini. He wanted regime change in Egypt and, mistakenly believed that Nasser would lose internal support if the canal zone was seized.

On Sunday, 14 October, Eden met General Maurice Challe, deputy chief of staff of the French Air Force. Challe outlined his plan that Israel attack the Suez Canal Zone and that Britain and France would "intervene" to separate the combatants, acting as peacekeepers to secure the canal zone.

Israel, already in conflict with Egypt over the Tiran Straits, feared a ban on their ships. Eden met Guy Mollet, Prime Minister of France, in Sèvres, agreeing, in secret, that Israel should attack Egypt to provide a reason for the Anglo-French forces to invade the canal zone. The Israeli attack began on 29 October. The next day, Britain and France issued ultimatums to the combatants to desist immediately. Fighting continued and the Anglo-French forces attacked on 5 November.

The military operation to seize the canal zone was well on the way to success but, before the whole zone could be secured, immense international pressure, headed up by Dag Hammarskjöld, UN Secretary General, forced a ceasefire at midnight on 6 November, primarily by threatening financial sanctions that would have damaged sterling profoundly. More damagingly to the occupying forces, the ceasefire insisted on their immediate withdrawal.

Health and Medication in the Months Before the Suez Crisis

We know from Evans that Eden's regular drug regime included the sedatives, sodium amytal grains 3 and Seconal enseal grains 1.5 at night and, Drynamyl one in the morning. Drynamyl contained amphetamine, a mood elevator and amylobarbitone, a sedative to counteract the side effects of amphetamine. Drynamyl formulated as a triangular tablet was colloquially known as "purple hearts". Another formulation, Drynamyl spansules ("Christmas trees") became a popular street drug in the 1960s and 1970s. Its medical use was discontinued in the 1970s.

We know Eden was also prescribed Promazine, an anti-psychotic to reduce anxiety and tension. In his biography of Eden, Robert Rhodes James refers to him having had to increase his dosage of sedatives and stimulants considerably in the months after Nassar nationalised the canal. Despite all this medication, he had a very poor sleep pattern, often waking at 3am. Some nights, if woken up by pain, he took Pethidine. He was also prescribed Benzedrine, an amphetamine, as a stimulant. Thomas describes Eden as practically living on Benzedrine. One observer describes him as being in a state of exaltation at times.

It is hard to believe that this cocktail of drugs did not affect his decision making adversely. It almost certainly goes some way to explaining why he acted out of character in that critical political era. With the benefit of hindsight, it is hard to believe that his doctors (who we know were consulted at least ten times between July and October that year) did not advise him to postpone major decision making but, maybe they tried unsuccessfully to do so. Astonishingly, it was less than two weeks after his major bout of cholangitis (on 5 October when he had a fever of 106° F), that he met Challe and the train of collusion began.

Owen firmly believes that a healthy Anthony Eden would not have made three crucially flawed decisions. These were, to collude with Israel, to mislead Eisenhower and, perhaps most astonishingly, to lie to the House of Commons. If the invasion had been postponed until after the US presidential election on 6 November, the American reaction might have been more muted. In the context of other world events, it allowed the Soviet Union to brutally suppress the Hungarian rising that began in October of that year. Western forces refrained from any intervention in Hungary.

When Eden died of prostatic cancer in 1977, *The Times* obituary said, "Eden was the last Prime Minister to believe Britain was a great power and the first to confront a crisis to prove she was not."

Further Reading

"The Effect of Prime Minister Anthony Eden's illness on his Decision Making During the Suez Crisis" by Lord David Owen. *QJM*, (2005), 98: 387-402

The Suez Affair by H. Thomas (Weidenfeld and Nicolson. 1986)

"Anthony Eden's (Lord Avon) Biliary Tract Saga" by John W. Braasch. *Annals of Surgery* (2003) 238: 7725

"Anthony Eden's Bile Duct: Portrait of an Ailing Leader" by G. Kune. *ANZ Journal of Surgery* (2003), 73: 341-5

Anthony Eden: Life and Reputation by D. Dutton (Hodder Arnold, London. 1997:423)

Anthony Eden by RR James (Weidenfeld and Nicolson, 1986:397)

Witch Hunts

A Medieval Obsession

"Thou shalt not suffer a witch to live" – **Exodus 22:18**

The Hassatan of Hebrew scripture had morphed into Satan, God's greatest adversary in the Book of Revelation. Theologians were inclined to dismiss magic and meetings with the devil as illusions but in the half century before John XXII, there had been more open discussion about magic and witchcraft.

Pope John XXII was elected after a consistory so protracted that Philip V shut up the cardinals in a convent, reducing their rations of food and drink daily until they elected a successor to Clement V.

In the early 14th century, John became exercised by the possible threat of black magic and witchcraft to the church. He set up a commission to look into these matters. Some years later, he issued a bull, *Super illius specula*, which proclaimed that any contact with demons or magic was heretical and could be investigated. However, it was a century later that witch hunting became widespread, coinciding with a marked reduction in the execution of heretics.

In 1484, Pope Innocent VII issued a bull, *Summis desiderantes affectibus*, on the matter of people who, "unmindful of their own salvation, have abandoned themselves to devils." When identified, such persons should be punished without let or hindrance.

A year later came an infamous book, *Malleus Malifacarum* (hammer of witches) by a Dominican, Heinrich Kramer, under the

Latin version of his name, Henricus Institoris. Another Dominican, Jacob Sprenger, had his name added as co-author 33 years after the first edition and 24 years after Kramer's death. There is still doubt about the veracity of Sprenger's involvement. He had been to the forefront in promoting devotion to the Rosary and had many clashes with Kramer when alive. While the book did not receive universal approval – being rejected by the Inquisition for example – it became the blueprint for later Christian (Catholic and Protestant) persecution of witches.

In Avignon, for the whole of his papacy, Innocent VII indulged in the good things of life, founding the vineyards of Chateauneuf de Pape. Avignon had become a fine city, with great financial clout in Europe by the end of his papacy. He became enormously fat due to prodigious eating. However, as his life drew to a close, he became more and more inert, to the extent that the only nourishment he could take was a few drops of milk from a woman's breast. In a desperate attempt to keep him alive, his Jewish doctor had three healthy men paid a ducat each to donate blood. The experiment failed but the ducats were prized from their fists, clenched in rigor mortis.

> *"Double, double, toil and trouble;*
> *Fire burn, and cauldron bubble" – Macbeth*

In Shakespeare's world, rural dwellers in particular believed in witches. White witches were good and healed people. Black witches were bad. They made a contract with the devil and so, were heretics.

After the Reformation, Christians of all denominations became more alert to witchcraft. Foremost in the fight against witchcraft was James VI of Scotland. Taking the crown at the age of 17 years, he was confirmed as head of the church in Scotland the following year. However, he felt threatened by extreme Protestant leaders.

In August 1589, James was married by proxy to Princess Anne of Denmark. She embarked on the five-day voyage to Scotland. The storms she encountered were so extreme that she ultimately diverted to Norway, landing in Oslo after 50 days at sea. Sensibly, it was decided to postpone her voyage to Scotland until the spring. James, somewhat recklessly, set sail from Leith, reaching Oslo after a stormy crossing a month later. James and Anne were then married in person but stayed in Denmark until the spring.

The Danes were convinced that the storms that had beset the royal couple were so extreme as to be only credibly due to witchcraft. Six witches were identified, tried, and executed in Denmark.

On the return crossing in the spring, severe storms were again encountered, almost sinking the royal vessel. James became convinced that witchcraft was responsible. He became obsessed with rooting it out.

Agnes Sampson from North Berwick was arrested and, under torture, confessed before the King that she christened a cat with a coven of other witches, before throwing it into the sea to cause a storm. She averred that only their strong Christian faith had saved the royal couple from drowning. Tried and convicted, she was garrotted publicly in front of Edinburgh castle and her body was burned.

By attending the trial, James made it a newsworthy event. James closely followed the further North Berwick trials, where confessions were extracted under torture, convictions arrived at and executions performed. His interest and involvement lent legitimacy to the trial process.

A pamphlet, *Newes from Scotland*, was published giving lurid details of the North Berwick trials. James then published his own book, *Daemonology*, setting out his understanding as to what constituted witchcraft and how to identify a witch. Specifically, there must be a pact with the devil, renouncement of baptism and the presence of a devil's mark on the witch's body. The devil's mark could, however, be difficult to find and could even be hidden in a body cavity, such as the vagina.

Another feature of witchcraft was communicating with the dead by summoning up the spirit as an apparition or, by raising them bodily from the dead, to use the deceased as a weapon (necromancy). In identifying a witch, he recommended in particular, searching for the devil's mark or trial by water. It did his reputation in England no harm at all that the *Newes from Scotland* pamphlet claimed, that the devil had told a coven of witches that the reason he tried so hard to harm the King was because he was his greatest enemy on earth.

When James became James I of England on the death of Elizabeth I, his interest in witchcraft waned. This, however, had little effect on witch hunting in Scotland over the next 70 years. Incidentally, the Scottish Kirk have the dubious honour of being the first to use sleep deprivation as a form of torture.

Identification of a Witch

The accused appeared stripped naked, with body hair shaved, in front of the magistrates. Any physical anomaly was scrutinised to try to identify a devil's mark. The mark was thought to result from contact with the devil's claw. Birthmarks, moles and tattoos were suspect. The mark was then subject to pricking, as it was supposedly insensitive to pain. If no devil's mark was found, professional pickers would search for areas of numbness throughout the body. They almost invariably found such an area, possibly by the ruse of using some blunted needles. Such a finding substituted for finding a visible devil's mark.

Another blemish looked for was the devil's teat. It was believed that witches fed imps and familiars (often dogs) from this teat. The devil himself was said to suckle on the teat while impregnating his servants. The offspring, Cambion, would reach adulthood on the seventh day of the seventh week of suckling and then wreak havoc. As all humans, male and female, have an embryonic milk line, supernumerary nipples (polythelia) are not uncommon. These occur in up to 1 in 18 humans. Usually, there is a single extra nipple, more commonly in men than women but, up to eight are recorded. Finding such a nipple would have convinced the magistrates they had found a witch's teat.

The touch test involved the accused touching a victim during a fit. If the fit stopped, they were deemed guilty. If it did not, they were innocent.

As all witches were said to renounce Baptism, ordeal by water was another way to identify them. It was believed that pure water would reject a witch. The suspect was tied up in a ritual fashion and then, typically, lowered by rope from a boat. If they floated, they were guilty. If innocent, they would sink and then be pulled back to the surface. Inevitably, there was a significant risk that the suspect would drown.

The prayer test involved the suspect reciting a piece from the Bible, or a prayer – usually the Lord's Prayer. Any mistake was taken as proof of guilt, even if the suspect was illiterate or terrified. In Salem, the Reverend Thomas Burroughs recited the Lords' Prayer clearly and without a mistake. Despite passing the prayer test he was still hung. The excuse for ignoring the result was that he must have been prompted by the devil himself to get it right!

Salem

In January 1692, Abigail Williams, aged 11 and Betty Parris, the niece and daughter of the Reverend Samuel Parris, Minister in Salem, Massachusetts, began to have strange fits, unlike those seen in epilepsy. They screamed, made animal-like sounds and threw things around. They claimed they were being pinched and pricked. The local doctor was unable to find a physical explanation.

Soon, other local girls began exhibiting similar behaviour. It was a time of significant political turmoil. William and Mary had been acclaimed as joint Sovereigns in England, following the ousting of Mary's father, James II. The existing royal charters were rendered void. It was not until February 1692 that a new governor of Massachusetts, William Phips, was sworn in in Boston.

The New England Puritans lived in scattered isolated settlements. They had much to worry about in their isolated, smoke-filled cabins. They believed in predestination. Only God could decide one's fate. Attacks from hostile Native American tribes, sometimes encouraged by the French, were a constant threat. Infant and maternal mortality were high.

Salem village was a fractious place. Parris was made minister after his three predecessors had left over various disputes. One, Samuel Burroughs, was later hung despite passing the prayer test. Parris did not endear himself to his congregation by his tardiness in accepting the post. He made matters worse by insisting several prominent church members do public penance.

The first arrests were made in March. Sarah Good, Sarah Osborne and Tituba, a slave girl who may have come from Venezuela via Barbados, were detained and tortured. They would have been seen as being on the fringes of society. Four more were accused that month including a four-year-old girl, who supposedly confessed to witchcraft. Two more women were arrested in April as was the husband of one, who questioned the validity of the court. The flood waters really opened when three of the next group arrested confessed to being witches and began naming accomplices. By August, detainees included many prominent citizens of high standing in the church.

No doubt, personal grievances were behind the naming of accomplices. As witches who confessed were not executed, it may have been a pragmatic choice to confess. Executions by hanging took place in June, July, August and September.

An 81-year-old farmer, Giles Covey, refused to enter a plea and was sentenced to undergo the torture of *peine forte et dure*. Progressively, more and more heavy stones were placed on his chest. He died, crushed to death, in 48 hours. In all, 14 women and five men were hung. They were denied Christian burial. Two dogs were hung. Governor Phips halted the trials in October. Much of the evidence leading to conviction was "spectral". Those afflicted testified to recognising an apparition of their tormentor.

More than 300 years later, in 2001, all those executed and charged were proclaimed innocent by the then Governor of Massachusetts. The cause of this horrendous episode in American history was probably mass psychological illness, formerly called hysteria. Settling of old scores and historic family feuds played some part. Various medical explanations, such as ergotism from contaminated rye, have been proposed but none are credible. Not a single one of those who sat in judgment had any legal training.

Between 1400 and 1800, forty to fifty thousand died in Europe and colonial America following conviction for witchcraft. Killings began when the burning of heretics tailed off. The present-day perception of the witch as a bent old crone was not the case.

Some voices of reason tried to halt the frenzy. Johannes Weyer, in the 16th century in Arnhem Holland, campaigned against the practice. He considered most accused were suffering mental illness rather than being possessed by the devil. He argued that confessions obtained on the rack or under other types of torture, such as thumbscrews, were extremely dubious. He was critical of clergy joining in the practice of torture, rather than giving support to those in mental turmoil. He had some initial success but, little is known of his final years, when he appears to have been forced to withdraw from medical practice.

Balthazar Beckker of the Dutch Reform Church spoke out against witch hunting in a book in 1691. He was not thanked by his fellow clergymen.

Killings actually climaxed in Europe in the late 18th century. In Catholic Poland, the execution rate for convicted witches, which had stood at around 4%, jumped to 50%. The driving force was largely the established churches, both Catholic and Protestant.

Further Reading

The Popes by John Julius Norwich (Vintage, London. 2012)

A History of Christianity by Diarmaid MacCulloch (Penguin Books, London. 2010)

Shakespeare's Restless World by Neil MacGregor (Penguin Books, London. 2014)

"Humane" Judicial Killing
The Guillotine; the Electric Chair

Joseph Ignace Guillotin, a medical doctor, opposed the death penalty. He accepted however that, in the fevered atmosphere of the French Revolution, this would remain an aspiration. Failing its abolition, he looked for an alternative to breaking on the wheel, hanging, quartering, drowning and other savage ways of ending a criminal's life. He also wanted to remove the perceived privilege of aristocrats to be executed by the blade. The first guillotine was set up in Paris, in 1792.

Alfred P Southwick, a dentist and his collaborator, George E Fell, promoted judicial killing by administering electric shock. With others, he designed a chair resembling a dental one with restraints. Condemned persons would be administered lethal electrical shock using alternating current (AC). His proposals were set in motion following a series of botched hangings in New York State. The electric chair was first used in New York in 1890.

Madame la Guillotine/La Veuve (The Widow)
Joseph-Ignace Guillotin was born in 1738, at Santes in southern France. He took his medical degree in the University of Paris. Entering politics, he achieved prominence in the Constituent Assembly from 1789. Accepting capital punishment would continue in France, he pursued alternatives to the burning at the stake, hanging, quartering, drowning and other slow methods. These were all designed to cause suffering to the condemned. As well as aiming for a swift and sure method of administering the

death penalty, he wished to remove the exclusive right of aristocrats to be executed by the sword or axe.

Antoine Louis, a surgeon, is credited with the invention of the guillotine as we know it. It comprises a wooden frame in which a weighted, angled blade is raised to the top. The victim is secured below the neck in line with the blade. The executioner releases the blade, decapitating the victim whose head falls into a basket. The method was seen by the revolutionary public to demonstrate equality in death. It remained the standard method of execution in France until the abolition of the death penalty there in 1981. It was used in colonial France. The author has seen one on display in Ho Chi Minh City, Vietnam.

Though he did not invent it, Guillotin's name became synonymous with the apparatus. This distressed him and his family. On his death, in 1814, the family petitioned the French Government to change its name. They were refused so, they changed their family surname instead.

Guillotin himself was imprisoned and might well have suffered the ultimate fate from his eponymous machine, had Robespierre not been toppled. Freed in a general amnesty, Guillotin forsook politics and resumed the practice of medicine.

Easily the most notable among those who fell victim to 'Madame la Guillotine' was Louis XVI. He was subjected to a show trial. All deputies who voted pronounced him guilty. By a majority of one, they later voted that his sentence should be death.

On 21 January 1793, he was driven in a carriage to the Place de la Révolution (later renamed Place de la Concorde) to be executed. He was accompanied by his Irish priest, the Abbé Edgeworth. The Abbé's father, a Church of Ireland clergyman, had converted to Roman Catholicism and moved from Ireland to Toulouse. His son was educated by the Jesuits before entering the priesthood.

Louis endured an hour's travel from the Temple, where he was imprisoned, to the scaffold. He is said to have asked on the journey, "Is there any news of La Perouse?"

La Perouse, an explorer from Albi, had disappeared on a scientific voyage around the world that had Royal patronage. A young Napoleon Bonaparte, then intent on a naval career, had applied for a position on the expedition but was not selected. The wrecks of the two ships in the expedition were identified off the Solomon Islands in the Pacific, in 2008.

There is a tradition that the Abbé said, "Son of St Louis, ascend to Heaven" as the blade fell. Henri Sanson, the executioner, attested to the serenity displayed by the King. Loud drum rolls prevented him from addressing the crowd. Sanson related that Louis' last words were "Sir, I am innocent of all that has been imported to me; I wish that my blood cement the French people." He was 38 years old.

Marie Antoinette, his queen, was moved from the Temple to the Concierge on the Isle de France. Here, she had no privacy and was under constant surveillance. Her eight-year-old son, Louis, was taken forcibly from her and placed in the care of a cobbler. On 16 October 1793, she was found guilty on a number of trumped up charges. These included incest – supposedly revealed by her son. Conveyed humiliatingly in a cart, her hands tied behind her by a leather leash, she was executed the same day.

George Jacques Danton, a leading figure early in the reign of terror voted for the King's death. He was condemned to death for venality and showing leniency towards enemies of the Republic. Maximilian Robespierre, who pushed for the execution of the King and Danton, was himself sent to the guillotine in 1794. He is credited with the motto Liberté, Égalité, Fraternité.

Charlotte Corday, herself a republican, gained access to Jean-Paul Marat by pretending that she would supply him with names of opponents of the revolution who should be executed. She held Marat responsible for the September Massacres (2-7 September 1792) and felt he was leading the revolution in the wrong direction.

Marat had a skin disease causing intolerable generalised itching, most probably Dermatitis herpetiformis. He got some relief in his bath so, had a desk top fitted to it allowing him to work while bathing. Corday stabbed him to death. She was executed four days later. Jacques Louis David painted a picture of Marat stabbed in his bath. This powerful oil painting is sometimes described as the first propaganda painting.

Hitler favoured the guillotine. In the last year of World War II, some 10,000 people were executed in this manner by the Nazis.

The Electric Chair

In 1878, Thomas Edison founded an electric light company powered by direct current electricity (DC). In 1884, Nikola Tesla joined Edison. They later fell out and George Westinghouse bought out Tesla's electric patents. Tesla was subsequently hired by Westinghouse and developed alternating current electricity (AC).

Alternating current was capable of transmission over hundreds of miles, as opposed to a mile or so for direct current. Edison did everything he could to discredit AC. This led to "the war of the currents", with Westinghouse fighting back. Edison maintained AC was far more dangerous than DC. Part of his campaign later involved him recommending the use of AC to power the electric chair and fix the danger of this in the public mind.

Alfred P Southwick, a dentist and George Fell, a physician, did a series of experiments in which they killed stray dogs by electric shock. A series of botched hangings led the governor of New York State to set up a commission to investigate more humane ways of administering capital punishment.

Southwick proposed a seat similar to a dental chair, with electric shock being delivered through electrodes attached to the restrained victim. He was on the commission and, in 1888, a version of his prototype, now called the electric chair, was recommended for use in New York. Edison was consulted and advised the use of AC current, using Westinghouse generators. Despite stringent objections from Westinghouse, this method was adopted.

Initially electrodes were placed on the head and back. William Kemmler was the first person executed in this manner, in 1890. It took eight minutes before he was pronounced dead. Westinghouse remarked they would have done better with an axe! Despite this, the electric chair rapidly gained popularity and replaced hanging in most states. Since the 1980s, lethal injection has become the favoured method. The electric chair is retained in many states as a backup or alternative.

Notable Executions

In 1946, Willie Francis, a 16-year-old black youth, was sentenced to death in Louisiana. He was charged with the murder of Andrew Thomas, a pharmacist, nine months before. After a short trial, an all-white jury found him guilty. The evidence was flimsy in the extreme.

In May of that year, he was seated in an electric chair nicknamed "Gruesome Gertie". After an electric current was passed through his body, the teenager shouted from under his facial hood that he could not breath. The hood was removed and, it was clear that he had survived the shock. An incorrect set up of the chair was blamed.

A new, enthusiastic attorney took on his case. Ultimately the case was referred to the Supreme Court. The appeal was rejected.

Francis was returned to the electric chair and successfully executed a year later. He was 18 years old.

Julius Rosenburg and his wife Ethel were accused of spying for the Soviet Union. Both had been members of the Communist Party. It was inferred that the information passed to Russia had speeded up the development of a nuclear bomb there. This is highly unlikely, however.

Julius did spy for the Russians. Ethel was never a spy but assisted her husband in various ways. Both were convicted and sentenced to death. It was generally perceived that the death sentence handed out to Ethel was designed to put pressure on Julius to reveal a spy ring. He did not.

Despite numerous international appeals for clemency, both were executed by electric chair in Sing Sing, New York on the same day in 1953.

Richard Hauptmann, a German carpenter, was convicted of the abduction and killing of Charles, the infant son of the aviator Charles Lindberg. The evidence was entirely circumstantial. Hauptmann was apprehended when he used some of the ransom money in a gas station. Hauptmann insisted on his innocence throughout. He was executed in April 1936.

His widow, Anna, fought to have the conviction overturned right up to her own death, aged 95. She was unsuccessful. In recent times it has been suggested that the aviator himself was complicit in the affair, as the infant was possibly retarded. This would not have fitted in with Lindberg's image as an Aryan. He was a great admirer of Hitler and did his utmost to keep the USA out of World War II. He had five more legitimate children. He fathered children with two German sisters and his secretary out of wedlock.

Topsy was a female elephant smuggled into the USA from southeast Asia. She was part of a troop of performing elephants in the Forepaugh and Sell circus. She gained a reputation as a "bad" elephant, attacking several handlers.

In 1902, a spectator, James Fielding Blount, gained entry to the circus menagerie. He may well have been intoxicated at the time. It is thought that he threw sand into Topsy's eyes and burned the tip of her trunk with a cigar. Topsy threw him to the ground with her trunk and crushed him to death.

Forepaugh and Sell sold her on to a Coney Island amusement park, whose owner later passed her on to his successors, Thompson and Dundy. Her handler, Ali, was prone to drunkenness and took to riding the animal along the streets of Coney Island. He even induced her to attack a police station. Ali was fired.

Thompson and Dundy could not even give the elephant away. Even the ASPCA refused to take her. They decided to kill her publicly by a combination of electric shock, poisoning, and strangulation. Copper lined sandals were placed on the right-fore and left-hind foot. Nooses attached to a winch were put around her neck. She was fed cyanide laced carrots. High voltage AC electric current was delivered to the sandals. Topsy fell over in seconds and the nooses were tightened. The event was filmed.

There is a popular misconception that the elephant killing was part of the "war of the currents". This is completely incorrect. Edison was, by then, no longer involved in the electrical company that bore his name and Westinghouse, likewise, had moved on. The "war of the currents" had concluded a decade before the elephant killing.

Conclusion

It is something of a paradox that the guillotine and the electric chair came into being as perceived "humane" alternatives to other methods of judicial killing.

Joseph-Ignace Guillotin left politics to resume medical practice after the eponymous apparatus had become the standard French instrument of state execution. On his death, in 1814, his family petitioned the French government to change its name. They were refused so changed their family name instead. France abolished the death penalty in 1981.

Southwick and Fell believed death by electrocution would be rapid certain and humane compared to alternatives. A variety of names were given to individual chairs, including Old Smokey, Old Sparky, Gruesome Gertie and Yellow Mama. The electric chair is now a secondary method of execution in a number of US States.

Further Reading
"Death of Joseph-Ignace Guillotin" in *History Today* (March 2014), vol 64 p9

Embalming
Pharaohs, Popes, Politicians

When I studied anatomy in UCC, there were two porters in the dissecting room. The senior was clearly the preferred one by the Professor of Anatomy. The junior, miffed by this, used to inform us that, unlike his superior, "I have me embalmers."

He had, indeed, achieved a diploma in embalming in the United Kingdom. Little did we know that, hidden under the floorboards of the pathology lecture theatre, lay an Egyptian mummy in a sarcophagus. It was apparently placed there on the orders of Professor Billy O'Donovan, Professor of Pathology, to avoid awkward questions. Alternatively, it may have been part of a former Medical Museum. The mummy is now stored in the Boole Library in UCC but is not on public display. In this, it shares the fate of Ramses II, removed from public view in the Egyptian Museum in Cairo by Anwar Sadat, who felt that having the mummy on display was disrespectful to that glorious pharaoh.

While we tend to historically associate embalming with Egyptian mummification, it was also practiced in China and Peru. Dry, cool conditions were required to preserve these mummified humans in the long term.

The Egyptians were free of taboos when it came to dealing with the human corpse. They believed the heart was the seat of the soul, memory and emotion and consequently, this organ was not removed. The brain was removed using hooks inserted through the nose and discarded. Evisceration of the body cavity was carried out through small incisions. The material removed was placed in canopic jars. These jars were so-called because of the resemblance to human headed jars found in Canopis, an ancient city near Alexandria.

Champollion, who famously deciphered ancient Egyptian script, investigated a Canopic jar as a 21-year-old assistant working in Grenoble. He immersed the jar in boiling water to melt the embalming fluid and retrieved an organ. This proved the function of these jars, which had previously been a matter of speculation.

Classically, four jars were present in the tomb. Each had a different head which guarded specific organs. The Ape head guarded the lungs, the Jackal – the stomach, the Falcon – the intestines and the Human (usually female) – the liver. Champollion believed that the Canopic deities had a role on the day of judgement when the heart was weighed against the feather of Maat (Truth).

Like the Egyptians, the Incas also believed in the importance of preserving the body intact after death. When Pizarro offered Atahualpa the choice of being burnt at the stake as a heretic or converting and being garrotted, he chose the latter. Despite this, Pizarro later burnt the body in any case.

Jews and Muslims do not allow embalming or cremation and recommend interment within 24 hours if possible. Notable exceptions were Joseph and his father Jacob, who were apparently embalmed in the Egyptian fashion.

> *"And when Joseph saw this, he fell up on his father's face, weeping and kissing him. And he commanded his servants, the physicians, to embalm his father. And while they were fulfilling his commands, there passed forty days; for this was the manner with bodies that were embalmed, and Egypt mourned for him seventy days." –* **Genesis 50:1-3**

Similarly, Joseph:

*"And he died being one hundred and ten years old. And
being embalmed, he was laid in a coffin in Egypt."*
— **Genesis 50:25**

The Process of Mummification

The body was dehydrated using natron, a natural preservative. The brain and internal organs were removed as already described. The corpse was washed with wine and the body cavities stuffed with bags of natron. Resin was poured into the skull cavity. The dehydration process took 40 days. Over the next 30 days, oils were applied and often a golden resin. The body was wrapped in bandages.

Pharaohs and wealthy people often had a burial mask placed on their head. This sometimes led to unfortunate results, such as in the case of Tutankhamun where the head was hacked off so that the mask could be removed from the mummy.

European embalming dates back to Crusader times, when many nobles wanted their bodies preserved to enable burial at home. It was used by anatomists to preserve specimens (the technique being somewhat different to that used in mummification). The discovery of formaldehyde in 1869 revolutionised matters and it replaced older chemicals, such as arsenic.

Currently, embalming is usually performed in the West to "sanitise the body" and make it more presentable for viewing by relatives and friends. It is thought that this may help in the grieving process. Chemicals are pumped into the carotid artery and drained from the jugular vein. The body cavities can be embalmed by aspirating the viscera and injecting formaldehyde into the chest and abdomen.

Notables Embalmed

Communist leaders have frequently been embalmed and put on display. Most famously Lenin's body can be seen in a mausoleum in Moscow. His body is kept at a constant low temperature with muted lighting. Maintenance is said to be carried out several times a week. It seems probable that many cosmetic touches have been added to his face over the years.

When Stalin died, in 1953, he was also embalmed and initially entombed alongside Lenin. After Khrushchev's famous speech, which commenced "De-Stalinization" in Russia, the body was removed and buried in the Kremlin Wall.

Mao Zedong (died 1976) is in a mausoleum in Tiananmen Square in Beijing. This was built on the site of the Gate of China, which was the principal entrance to the Royal Palace. It has been suggested that what viewers actually see is a wax cast, which has been placed over Mao's body, although this has been hotly denied by the Chinese.

Kim Il-sung (died 1994) and Kim Jong-il (died 2011) lie in state in a mausoleum in The Palace of The Sun. This was formally Kim Il-sung's office in Pyongyang, North Korea. Also lying in state in this mausoleum, are the late leaders' cars, train compartments, a yacht and even Kim Jong-il's platform shoes.

Abraham Lincoln (died 1865) was embalmed after being assassinated by John Wilkes Booth at Ford's Theatre in Washington. This enabled the body to be moved by train over several days to his home town of Springfield, Illinois.

In 1901, the body was disinterred, at the expressed wish of his son, who feared that it would be stolen, before reburying it in a concrete vault. The coffin was opened and observers state that Lincoln's features were still clearly evident.

Booth suffered a broken leg following the assassination and was taken by an accomplice to the farm of Dr Samuel A. Mudd, who set the fracture. Mudd was later convicted by a military tribunal on a split vote, narrowly missing the death penalty. Instead, he was sent to a military prison, Fort Jefferson, on an island in the Gulf of Mexico. He was issued a pardon by Andrew Johnson. The derogatory phrase 'His name is Mudd' derived from this physician's name.

David Livingston (died 1873) expired of dysentery and malnutrition two years after being rediscovered by Henry Morton Stanley. Determined to prove that he had discovered the source of the Nile (in fact he had not), he continued exploring ultimately in the company of only two faithful servants. Following his death, they buried his heart and embalmed the body. These two servants carried it 1,500 km over land and eventually, entrusted it to the Livingstone relief party, who brought it home for burial in Britain.

Diana, Princess of Wales (died 1997) who perished in a motor vehicle accident was embalmed to prevent decomposition in the heat of Paris in August. Conspiracy theorists speculated, amongst other things, that this was done to destroy any evidence of pregnancy.

Botched Embalming
Many popes have been successfully embalmed. The process has been made more difficult since Pius X (died 1914) prohibited removal of internal organs, which had been standard practice in the process of preserving the body. (He had also denounced modernism and returned church music to plainsong and the Gregorian Chant, removing works by Rossini and Verdi from contemporary church music). Despite these non-binding restrictions, popes such as John XXIII (died 1963) remain well preserved following embalming.

When Pius XII died in 1958, his embalming was undertaken by a controversial eye doctor, Galeazzi Lari. Lari was a favourite of Mother Pasqualina, the nun who had run the papal household for several decades despite several attempts by Pacelli's family, particularly his sister Elisabetta, to oust her. Some indication of her hold over the Pope is the story that she had burst in on an audience with John Foster Dulles (the American Secretary of State) to inform the Pope that his soup was getting cold!

Galeazzi Lari consulted a little-known dentist in Rome about the Pope's anxiety that his gums were softening. This dentist recommended that he take large amounts of chromic acid to "strengthen his gums". Almost certainly, this caused oesophageal ulceration, leading to severe bouts of hiccup, which became a feature of his later years, being noticed by many during papal audiences.

Lari also called in a Swiss practitioner, Dr Nichaus, who injected the Pope with 'living' foetal cells from sheep and monkeys, which Nichaus claimed reversed the ageing process. When the Pope died, Pasqualina engaged Lari to carry out the embalming process. Lari announced that he was using a new embalming technique, "similar to that used on Jesus Christ."

Unfortunately, the body began to decompose rapidly. The hearse was first taken to St John Lateran, where a series of loud eructations emanated from the coffin, due to decomposition of the body. The lying-in-state in St Peter's took place over the next three days and saw the pontiff's face turn green and then purple. The stench from the body was so great that a Swiss Guard fainted. The final indignity occurred when the Pope's blackened nose fell off. The face was then covered with white silk prior to the coffin lid being sealed with gold nails.

Disease in Ancient Egypt

Techniques such as CT scanning and DNA analysis have revealed much about disease prevalent in Egyptian mummies. Perhaps the most detailed studies have been done on Tutankhamun. These studies have been hampered by the fact that the head was hacked from the body to retrieve the funerary mask, the upper limbs were severed to remove jewellery and both lower limbs were also removed at the pelvis.

Studies have, however, been done following reconstruction, in so far as it was possible, of the pharaoh's mummy. While controversy still exists as to the precise cause of his death, it is now established that he was 19 years of age at the time of demise. He, like many others studied from that period, had evidence of malaria, which was rampant in Egypt. Specifically, he had a healed jaw fracture, a small cleft palate and a familial elongated skull. There was an unhealed fracture of one leg and unusually, the sternum and ribs were missing.

There is speculation that he may have suffered from Marfan's or Klinefelter's Syndrome. It has been suggested by Timmann and Meyer that he was homozygous recessive for the sickle cell gene. The discovery of walking canes and medicines in the tomb suggest that he had a problem with his gait. While most believe he had a natural death, others speculate that he was poisoned by a rival. What is certain is that early suggestions he had been murdered by a blow to the skull have been comprehensively disproved. It is also possible that he died after a fall from his horse-drawn chariot and this would be supported by the absence of his sternum and the unhealed fracture of his femur.

Many studies confirm that atherosclerosis was common in ancient Egypt. Miyamoto et al. (2009) in a study of 22 mummies showed atherosclerosis in more than 50% with identified arteries. The disease worsened with age and was seen in both males and females. They speculate on the role of diet and, in particular, the probable high salt intake of these mummies, who were the remains of close associates of the pharaoh in his court. Salt was used extensively at that time to preserve meat.

Another mummy, in the University of Zagreb, appears to have suffered from Hand Schuller Christian Disease.

Severe dental caries were identified in a mummy, now in McGill University, Canada. This young male had a large cavity which had been packed with a linen pack, probably soaked in painkilling medication.

Further Reading

Tutankhamen's Curse: The developing history of an Egyptian king by Joyce Tyldesley (Profile Books. 2012)

Tattoos

Think Before You Ink

The word tattoo is derived from the Tahitian verb, *tatau*, meaning "to mark".

As a medical student in the Royal London Hospital in Whitechapel, in the late 1950s, I recall Sir (later Lord) Russell Brain, the neurologist had a rule for outpatients. He would instruct us to do a WR blood test for syphilis on any outpatient with a tattoo (or, indeed, any male patient who did not remove his hat in his presence!).

Tattoos were then associated with seamen, criminals and prostitutes. Since the mid-1970s, the scenario has changed radically. Tattoos are ubiquitous in the West and now fail to even shock. It is estimated that 20 per cent of British adults have a tattoo. Some, such as David Beckham, the soccer player, have innumerable ones including, in his case, his wife, Victoria's name misspelled in Hindi.

In fact, the history of tattooing goes back to the Stone Age. Direct evidence of tattooing on human mummified skin came with the chance finding of Otzi, the Iceman in the Otztal Alps in Italy in 1991. Estimates are that Otzi was born around 3300 BCE. He has 61 tattoos. The pigment came from ash or soot. Many of the tattoos are linear. The majority are on his lower limbs. It is speculated that they may represent an attempt at pain relief. If so, they predate the first known use of acupuncture in China by 2000 years.

We know tattoos existed in Peru, Egypt and the Philippines as far back as 2000 BCE. Tattooing is prohibited in the Bible:

> *"You shall not make any cuttings in your flesh for the dead, neither shall you make in yourselves any figures or mark: I am the Lord."* – **Leviticus XIX 28**

In the West, it was Captain James Cook who introduced the word tattoo into the English language, when he returned from an expedition to Polynesia. The pre-existing word "tap too" referred to a drum beat. Cook observed that the technique used in Tahiti involved scarification with sharpened bone and shell to impart the tattoo.

In 1774, he brought back a tattooed Polynesian. When asked his name, he replied, "O Mai" meaning *of the family of Mai*. Mistaking the particle "o" for part of the name, the officers called him "Omai". He proved a sensation in London, being presented to George III. He was painted by Sir Joshua Reynolds, in a classic outfit with a turban quite unlike anything he would have worn in Tahiti. The picture was exhibited in the Royal Academy in 1776, to much critical acclaim. The painting is now owned by John Magnier. Magnier was refused an export licence to bring the painting to Ireland. He in turn refused to sell it to the Tate. A temporary loan to the Irish National Gallery ended in 2012. The painting is currently due to go on show in an exhibition in the Rijksmuseum in Amsterdam.

Many of Cook's crew were tattooed, starting a tradition among seamen. Over time, a sailor's tattoos came to indicate areas of service. An anchor indicated the Atlantic; a turtle, crossing the Equator and a dragon, a China station.

Later, tattooing – a very expensive procedure at the time – was favoured by royalty and the upper classes. Bertie, later King Edward VII, had a large one of a Jerusalem cross inked when in Damascus. Both his sons, including the one who was later George V, were tattooed in Japan, returning from a tour of Australia. Jennie Churchill, mother of Winston, had a serpent tattoo on her wrist. She usually covered this with a diamond bracelet. A Scottish

Baron went further, having a copy of Constable's etching, *Mrs Pelham*, after Reynolds, tattooed on his chest at enormous expense.

The technique was revolutionised with the introduction of an electric tattoo machine, developed and patented by an Irish-American, Samuel O'Reilly, in New York. This made the technique more widely available and affordable. It was only in the 1970s that it became mainstream. A recent poll in the USA indicated tattooed women outnumbered men for the first time.

Gottfried Lindaur, a Czech artist who moved to New Zealand, painted many Maori chiefs accurately recording their facial tattoos. Charles Frederick Goldie, a native-born New Zealand artist made a speciality of painting Maori chiefs of high standing. An art forger, Karl Sim, changed his name by deed poll to "C F Goldie" to sign forgeries of Goldie's work. His autobiography was appropriately called "Good as Goldie".

Medical Issues
Many adults and most adolescents give no consideration to associated medical risks. Peer pressure is common and, selection of a tattoo parlour is often the result of discussion with those who have already undergone the procedure, rather than with a health professional. It is not widely known that in the Republic of Ireland, tattoo parlours are entirely unlicensed and not subject to any public health scrutiny. Neither is there any regulation of the training of tattoo artists.

Health risks include localised infection, often with *staphylococcus aureus*. There are several reports of outbreaks of MRSA in the USA. Potential systemic infections include hepatitis C. In a study in Taiwan, 12.6% of 87 tattooed, healthy males without other risk factors, were anti-HCV positive, compared to 2.4% of matched controls.

Hepatitis B is a risk factor from infected needles. As tattoo artists are not obligated to be immunised against Hepatitis B, they are another possible risk factor. However, a study in the USA found Hepatitis B was more commonly acquired after dental procedures than visits to a tattoo parlour. HIV transmission is theoretically possible but, no definite case has ever been shown to be transmitted by the technique. *Bacterial endocarditis* has been reported. Local reactions, including keloid formation, can occur. Delayed local reactions are recorded. Pigment accumulation in lymph nodes may interfere with melanoma diagnosis.

The Irish Blood Transfusion Service do not accept donations for four months after tattoo or body piercing. In other jurisdictions, no donations are accepted for a year.

The Dark Side
It was common in China to tattoo the faces of criminals. In Japan, criminals were also tattooed on various body parts. Sherlock Holmes solved one of his earliest cases by recognising a tattoo on a villain.

Roald Dahl wrote a macabre short story featuring Drioli, a Russian tattoo artist. The then unknown artist, Chaim Soutine, is persuaded to paint a picture of Drioli's wife, Josie, on the tattooist's back and tattoo over it. Years later, Drioli, now down on his luck, passes an art gallery in Paris exhibiting the newly discovered Soutine's paintings. He enters the gallery, removes his shirt and shows the tattoo to the assembled crowd. One man offers to pay for skin grafting if he would consent to have the portrait removed. Another offers him luxury accommodation in his hotel in Cannes in return for Drioli displaying his back to guests. He accepts the second offer and goes to dinner with his new patron. He disappears. The hotel is fictional. Some months later, a heavily varnished painting matching that on Drioli's back is seen on sale in Buenos Aires!

During the Second World War, members of the Nazi Waffen SS (Armed Defence Force) had a 7mm tattoo on the underside of the left arm, indicating their blood group (but not the Rhesus status).

Its purpose was, if injured or unconscious and requiring transfusion, they would receive the correct blood group. After the war, the presence of such a tattoo was taken as evidence of membership of the SS and many tried to convince their captors that their blood group tattoo was their inmate tattoo – that they were victims rather than perpetrators. Not all SS members had the tattoo. Josef Mengele was one such and it probably helped him evade capture.

Horst Wessel, a Nazi thug whose myth was built up by Goebbels, was shot in the face by a heavily tattooed Communist, Ali Hohner. All those connected to Wessel's death (and many entirely innocent) were rounded up and executed (some by beheading). Others were sent to concentration camps. Hohner was dragged from his prison cell and murdered. No effort was made by the Nazis to apprehend Hohner's killers.

The practise of tattooing concentration camp inmates was introduced in Auschwitz. These were initially applied to the left upper chest. Later, they were placed on the left forearm. Marceline Loridan-Ivans, a survivor of Auschwitz-Birkenau, recalls her father's parting words, "You may come back – but I will not." She says that parting prophesy "burned into my mind as violently and definitively as the number 78750 tattooed on my left arm."

Tattooing is now ubiquitous in young adults and adolescents. Very few subjecting themselves to the procedure give much thought to health or associated social risks. If a health professional is consulted, it is important to be non-judgmental. A tetanus booster should be recommended. Advice on aseptic skin preparation and aftercare should be given. A tattoo parlour using disposable or properly sterilised needles should be selected. Ideally, the tattoo artist should be immunised against Hepatitis B. It should be pointed out that local anaesthetic is not used so, the inking can be painful. It should be stressed too that tattoo parlours in the Republic of Ireland are not licensed or subject to inspection by any health authority. Blood cannot be donated for four months after a tattoo.

Most who get a tattoo do not appreciate how difficult and expensive it is to have them removed. Laser removal is probably the best approach but even then, there may be considerable scarring. Young people should be encouraged to "think before you ink".

Further Reading

"Tattooed: By Royal Appointment" by Essie Fox in virtualvictorian.blogspot.com (8 March 2013)

"The Indelible Legacy of a Seafaring Heritage" by Tessa Dunlop in *History Today*, June 2012, p36-37

"It's Official: Otzi the Iceman has the oldest tattoos in the world" by Deter-Wolf et al in RedOrbit.com (2015)

Alice Though the Looking Glass

An Anatomical Conundrum

In the Michaelmas term of my Anatomy studies, in the first medical year, we dissected the upper limb. Professor Michael MacConaill (better known to us all as "an tOllamh") announced that he would conduct individual oral anatomy examinations in his office in the New Year. I carefully revised origins and insertions of muscles and the relationship of blood vessels and nerves in the upper limb. I read through my notes of his lectures on "spurt and shunt" muscle activity.

His eccentricity was already well known to us. He had stood in front of the class one day, upper arms at 90 degrees to his body, elbows bent with his forearms vertical, his hands facing upwards and fingers spread saying, "Gentlemen, I am a uterus and these are the fallopian tubes."

He had also announced one day, at FCA training, "Gentlemen, Cork has become an atomic target." (He was referring to the oil refinery in Whitegate.)

On the day of the viva, I was quietly confident. I stood outside the door of his office until there was an imperious call, "Enter". He stood there in his white laboratory coat with his back to me, gazing out at Cork gaol, (about which he published a poem, "A Ballad to Cork Gaol" in the *Dublin Opinion* magazine). Initially, I wondered if he was having one of his petit mal epileptic seizures. Then, he swung around to face me, the silver bag needle he used as a pointer swaying on its Petersham ribbon and said, "Whelton, are you familiar with *Alice Through the Looking Glass*?"

As Frankie Howard used to say, 'my gast had never been so flabbered!' For a moment, I felt like saying, 'I thought this was an anatomy oral' but instead, I replied, "Yes, Professor."

MacConaill wrinkled his nose, sniffed and then said, "Tell me about it."

I dredged my childhood memories and blurted out self-consciously, "Well, you see, there was this hedge under which Alice was sitting and nearby was a big rabbit hole. Suddenly a large, white rabbit appeared muttering, 'I'm late.' It ran past her and disappeared into the hole—"

"No, no, no," said MacConaill, "that is *Alice in Wonderland*. I asked you about *Alice Through the Looking Glass!*"

In the years since, I often puzzled over that question, trying to make some sense of it. The best analysis for me, to date, was that of Trevor Joyce in UCC, who speculated that perhaps MacConaill was indicating things are not always what they seem.

Charles Dodgson had asked his cousin and child friend, Alice Rakes, to "Come and see something puzzling." They went to his house where he handed her an orange and asked her, in which hand was she holding the fruit?

"The right," she said.

"Now go stand in front of the mirror and tell me which hand is holding the orange," said Dodgson.

She did so and said, "The left hand."

"Exactly," said Dodgson, "and how do you explain that?"

In reply she said, "Well, if I was on the other side of the glass, would not the orange still be in my right hand?"

"The best answer I have had yet," laughed Dodgson.

At the time of that anatomy examination, I was only dimly familiar with the Alice stories from my childhood and of course, like most children, my images were also based on the iconic Tenniel drawings. Since then, I have tried to enlighten myself about the extraordinary storyteller, Lewis Carroll, and his creator, the stuttering deacon logician, Charles Dodgson, who spent his entire adult life in Christchurch, Oxford, ultimately becoming reclusive and lonely.

Life and Times
Charles Lutwidge Dodgson was born, in 1832, into a High Church Anglican conservative family, in a parsonage in Cheshire. He had Irish connections. His great-grandfather became Bishop of Elphin and his military grandfather had been killed in action in Ireland, when Charles' father was an infant. His father was an Anglican cleric, much involved in the religious disputes of the time. He admired the Tractarian movement in Oxford and John Henry Newman. His mother was Francis Jane Lutwidge.

His first 11 years were spent in home education with his seven sisters and two brothers. In 1842, the family moved to a much more salubrious parish in North Yorkshire. Charles, like six of his seven sisters, had a severe stammer. It has been speculated that the dodo in Alice in Wonderland emanated from his stuttering efforts to pronounce 'Dodgson'.

He attended a boarding school in Richmond for two years before being sent to Rugby public school, at age 14. Though he was praised for his academic abilities, he disliked Rugby intensely, with its sports-dominated culture. He matriculated in Oxford in his father's old college, Christchurch, in 1850 and went into residence there in 1851. He graduated Bachelor of Arts with a first-class honours degree in 1854 and became lecturer in mathematics in Christchurch, in 1855. He was to remain there, in various capacities, until his death in 1878.

Lewis Carroll
His pseudonym came about as follows. Lewis was the anglicised version of Ludovicus, Latin for Lutwidge (his mother's surname)

and Carroll, an Irish surname similar to the Latin Carolus for Charles. He reversed Carolus Ludovicus, to become Lewis Carroll.

Deaf in one ear from a childhood illness, he was a chronic stammerer in the presence of adults but possibly not children. From an early age, he loved playing tricks and entertaining his siblings and other children.

As well as his enduring publications, he was a gifted photographer. While he is best known now for his photographs of nude or semi-nude adolescent girls, he also did photographic portraits of Tennyson, the Rossetti's and Ellen Terry. His photographic images of nude and semi-nude teenage girls have come in for much analysis. They must however be understood in the pervading Victorian concept that girls of that age were the ideal of virginal purity. Similar images were often used in Christmas cards of the time. He also, always obtained permission from the child's parents before taking the photographs and the mother was usually present at the time the images were made. Some have gone as far as calling him a paedophile but, this judgement is made by modern-day standards. He did, however, give up nude photography altogether in 1880, though he continued to sketch young girls and commission pictures of them from an artist friend.

In the day job, as a mathematics lecturer, he was a stickler for college rules. He always wore grey cotton gloves. William Tuckwell of New College commented that, "except to little girls, he was not an alluring personage."

Cohen & Green (1979) quoted from his letters, "A girl of about twelve is my ideal beauty of form and one hardly sees why the lovely forms of girls should ever be covered up."

He told a child, girl friend, "I am fond of children (except boys) and have more child friends than I could possibly count on my fingers."

The most famous of these child friends was to be Alice Liddell. In 1856, Henry Liddell was appointed Dean of Christ Church. In April, the twenty-four-year-old Dodgson took the first of many photographs of the three Liddell sisters, including the three-year-old Alice. He was a regular visitor to the deanery and the genesis of the Alice stories was in "fairy tales" made up for their entertainment. The most famous of these were first told on a boat trip up the Thames. He later referred to one such trip of three miles from Oxford to Godstow as that "golden afternoon". The three Liddell girls pleaded for stories and later, Alice begged him to write them down. Dodgson remained very close to the Liddell family, playing croquet, entertaining and photographing the children in the deanery.

Alice's mother abruptly terminated his familiarity when Alice was eleven years old. The rift may have had nothing to do with Alice but come about due to rumours of Dodgson been involved with her fourteen-year-old sister, Lorena, her governess or even the Liddell mother, Ina. His diary pages of that time have disappeared, possibly destroyed by his family and Mrs Liddell destroyed all his letters to Alice. There has been much speculation as to whether he was in love with Alice, to the point of making a proposal of marriage when she reached a suitable age. This seems unlikely. Indeed, he commented, after a chance encounter with Alice in Oxford after the rift, "she seems changed a good deal, and not for the better – probably going through the usual awkward stage of transition."

Through the Looking Glass

These tales come from a double narrative: a journey through the looking glass and a chess game. Many of the stories were based on those told to the Liddell children and not included in the original *Alice in Wonderland*. The children particularly remembered stories of chess pieces coming to life. These stories coincided with them learning to play chess in the Deanery. While the kings and queens in wonderland are based on playing cards, those in *Through the Looking Glass* are based on chess pieces. Alice herself was portrayed as a pawn.

As the book progresses, Alice moves across a living "chessboard", meeting many nursery rhyme characters such as Humpty Dumpty and the Tweedle brothers, as well as the lion and the unicorn. Chess piece characters include the awkward white knight (thought to be a self-portrait of Dodgson).

Alice finally reaches the eighth square, where she becomes "Queen Alice", only to protest at the disorder around her at her coronation banquet, where she ultimately pulled the table cloth, causing all the plates dishes and candles to crash onto the floor.

Conclusions

The only connection that I can make between the upper limb and *Alice Through the Looking Glass* is the mirror image of a hand holding an orange, shown in reverse. Dodgson was born left handed but forced to use his right hand and like Leonardo da Vinci, he obviously enjoyed mirror image writing. Indeed, the first verse of Jabberwocky in *Through the Looking Glass* is written in such a fashion, causing Alice to be puzzled initially: "Why, it's a looking glass book, of course! And if I hold it up to the glass, the words will go the right way again."

An tOllamh may also have been thinking of *Finnegans Wake*, where Joyce uses the image of Humpty Dumpty repeatedly as a metaphor for the fall of man in the guise of Tom Finnegan. Finnegan comes back to life at his wake, where whiskey (*uisce beatha* – water of life) is spilled over him, symbolising the resurrection of man.

When I met Professor MacConaill, several years later and asked him directly what he was getting at, with the question that he had posed to me in that first anatomy exam, about *Alice Through the Looking Glass*. He looked me straight in the eye and replied, "Haven't the faintest idea Whelton."

Though I am still ambivalent about the appropriateness of such a question, it has led me down a literature search with multiple spin-off benefits intellectually, if not anatomically.

Further Reading

Alice's Adventures in Wonderland and *Through the Looking Glass and What Alice Found There* by Lewis Carroll (Hugh Haughton's centenary edition. Penguin Books, London. 1998)

The Selected Letters of Lewis Carroll by Lewis Carroll with Roger Lancelyn Green and Morton N. Cohen (Palgrave Macmillan UK. 1979)

The Annotated Alice, by Martin Gardner (Penguin Books, London. 2001)

Finnegans Wake by James Joyce (Wordsworth Editions Ltd, London. 2012)

Richard Dadd

Murderer and Master Painter

The final line in my fifth-year school report was, "If Michael's Latin does not improve, he will not get into Medical School."

As Latin was obligatory for Medicine at the time, as a precaution, I was allowed to take the pass course. This meant I had to drop Applied Mathematics due to a clash in the timetable. I was allowed to take Art – or Drawing as it was then known. The Christian Brothers did not rate Art worthy of teaching to the honours class so, I attended the Crawford School of Art, one night a week, that year.

A previous student of the Cork School of Art was Daniel Maclise. Maclise worked in Newenham's Bank for two years before his artistic talent was spotted when he sketched the visiting Sir Walter Scott. He studied Art in Cork for two years and then went to London, being accepted as a pupil in the Royal Academy. He became a member of a sketching club called "the clique", illustrating several books for Dickens. A fellow member was Richard Dadd, who was considered the best draughtsman in the group. While Maclise concentrated on historical theme painting, Dadd painted from the imagination, specialising in fairy works.

In 1842, Dadd went as draughtsman on an expedition to the Middle East and Egypt. Initially, the trip went well with Dadd recording scenes in watercolour. On a boat journey on the Nile, he was thought to have suffered from sunstroke, becoming aggressive and delusional. His family arranged rest and recuperation in Kent but, the delusions persisted and worsened. He was almost certainly suffering from paranoid schizophrenia.

He became convinced that his father was possessed by the devil. In August 1843, he killed his father with a knife and fled to France, where he attempted to kill another visitor with a razor.

Returning to Britain, he admitted killing his father. He claimed to be a reincarnation of the Egyptian God Osiris. Committed to Bethlem Hospital (also known as Bedlam), enlightened medical staff fortunately allowed him to continue painting. Dickens liked to walk past Bedlam musing that the sane might resemble the insane at night. Here, Dadd produced his most famous watercolour, *The Fairy Fellers Master Stroke* – a vision of fairyland with small, meticulously painted figures dwarfed by blades of grass.

Controversially the term "outsider art" has been used to describe painters such as Dadd. However, his attention to detail preceded his incarceration and he painted conventional portraits of his doctors. It is probable that the character, Richard Babley in *David Copperfield* is named after Dicken's contemporary, Richard Dadd.

Putting a Foot in It

The Divine Sarah Bernhardt

In 2008, a French newspaper announced in banner headlines the "miraculous rediscovery" of Sarah Bernhardt's amputated leg, preserved in formalin, in Bordeaux. The Faculty of Medicine there countered with a statement that the leg was never really lost, only forgotten and promised to prepare it for display. Sarah had damaged her leg when she jumped from a parapet, supposedly of the Castel San Angelo in Rome, in the final scene of the play, *La Tosca*, in Rio de Janeiro in 1905.

Born in Paris to a Dutch Jewish courtesan mother, she was one of three daughters born out of wedlock. Her father's name is unknown. Her birth records were destroyed in a fire and she became a self-mythologiser. Sarah Bernhardt, "the divine Sarah", was the most famous actress of the 19th Century. She was arguably the world's first superstar, endorsing Pears soap and Columbia bicycles. She famously slept in a coffin to enhance her senses for tragic roles. On a tour of the USA, she travelled with a pet alligator called Ali Gaga. Primarily a tragedienne, she outraged society by playing, not only female but also male roles, such as Hamlet and Judas. She had numerous affairs, including one with Bertie, Prince of Wales, the future King Edward VII.

As a young actress in Paris, she took a medical student, Samuel Pozzi, as a lover. The affair lasted 10 years, on and off, until he married – but they remained lifelong friends. When the pain in her knee became intolerable in 1914, it was to Pozzi she turned. He put the knee in plaster in the hope that this would relieve pain and lead to a joint fusion. After six months, she was no better and begged him to do an amputation. By this time, she had moved to

Bordeaux on Clemenceau's insistence, as he was fearful that she would be captured if Paris fell to the Germans.

Pozzi was now a well-established gynaecological surgeon and asked a locally based, general surgical protégé, Jean Denuce to see her. Denuce removed the cast and diagnosed tuberculous osteoarthritis. Despite his reservations, especially as she was now 71 years of age, he finally agreed and did an above knee amputation in February 1915. His diagnosis was confirmed but fortunately, there was no evidence of tuberculosis elsewhere in her body.

Her fame was such that she reputedly refused an offer of 10,000 US dollars to allow the limb to be displayed and tour with a freak show. Now free of pain, she toured the front lines extensively, entertaining Allied troops. Finding the wooden prosthesis cumbersome, she took to being carried on stage in a gilded litter by two porters.

She toured the USA in 1916 and was a strong proponent of involving America in the war. She had rehearsed for the lead role in Oscar Wilde's play, *Salome*, in London only for the staging to be banned by Lord Chamberlain. She worked up until her death in 1923 and, like her friend, Oscar, was buried in Père Lachaise Cemetery in Paris.

But what of the long lost or forgotten amputated limb? When inspected by Bernhardt historians, they expressed doubts about its provenance. True, it was an amputated limb from 1915 but it was a below knee specimen and Bernhardt's was an above knee amputation. In addition, much to the embarrassment of the Faculty of Medicine in Bordeaux, it was a left leg and it was Bernhardt's right leg that had been amputated. As she herself may well have said, "Zoot alors!"

The Murder of Laura Cross
Done to Death by Poison

The hairs stood up on my neck when my father pointed out Shandy Hall one day, when we were fishing in Coachford. "That is the house where Dr Cross murdered his wife," he said.

Philip Henry Eustace Cross qualified as a medical doctor in the College of Surgeons. He joined the British Army, serving at the Siege of Sevastopol in the Crimean War, where he was promoted to Staff Surgeon. He was then posted to India during the Indian mutiny and later served in China. In all, he spent six years abroad as an army surgeon before he returned to England.

In 1869, at the age of 46, he married 29-year-old Mary Laura Marriot in London. Laura's family were wealthy landowners living in a mansion – Abbots Hall in Essex, part of a monastic property seized by Henry VIII and given to Thomas Cromwell. Despite his professional qualifications and ownership of a 500-acre estate, Laura's father did not approve the match so, there was no financial marriage settlement from him. After the marriage, they went to live in Canada, where Cross's Regiment was then stationed. When her father died a year later, she was left £5,000.

In 1875, Cross retired from the British Army on half pay with the rank of Surgeon Major. The family then moved to his family home, Shandy Hall, where Cross took on the role of gentleman farmer.

There were three daughters and two sons from the union. Two of the daughters were "not of strong mind" and suffered from epilepsy. The two boys were sent to boarding school in England while, the girls were home-schooled by a governess.

Laura herself was said to have a delicate constitution and suffered palpitations, raising fears that she had an underlying heart problem. She also had seizures, almost certainly due to epilepsy. Cross was a difficult person and fell out with many locals whereas, Laura was sociable and had a circle of friends. Despite this, it appears that she missed her family in England and was increasingly lonely in Shandy Hall.

Eveline Forbs Skinner (Effie) was born in 1865. Her father was a Scottish church minister. Though respectable, the family was impoverished and Effie was educated with a view to teaching and minding children of the privileged. In due course, Effie took up the position of governess to the Caulfield family, neighbours and friends of the Crosses.

In July 1886, Laura took an extended break at her family home in Essex. During her absence, Cross was a frequent visitor to the Caulfield home. He became infatuated with Effie finally kissing her one day, much to her embarrassment. However, there must have been a mutual attraction and a job offer to Effie came from Cross.

In October 1886, the 20-year-old Effie came as governess to Shandy Hall. Laura had now returned from England and must have suspected her husband was romantically involved with the governess. Dr Cross firmly denied any liaison. However, Laura insisted on dismissing Effie in January 1887. Effie took up another post in Carlow but Cross engaged in covert correspondence. They had a number of assignations in Dublin. Effie became pregnant that spring and delivered their son, John, in December 1887.

In May 1887, Laura developed vomiting and diarrhoea. Attacks were recurrent. Some were associated with severe thirst. Apart from a single visit by a retired doctor, Godfrey (a relation of Cross by marriage), no doctor other than Cross himself managed her illness. She died on Thursday, 2 June. Cross registered the death as typhoid fever. He buried her on Saturday, 4 June. He explained the rapid interment on the infective nature of her illness and his wish to avoid burying her on a Sunday, which he described as "the Papist's favoured day for burial."

The following week, he went to England, supposedly to inform the two sons of their mother's death. While there, he married Effie and returned with his new wife to Shandy Hall on 26 June. Not surprisingly, rumours swept through the local community. Detective Inspector Henry Tyacke (probably prompted by Effie's former employers, the Caulfields) requested a coroner's inquest and permission was granted to exhume the body buried seven weeks earlier. A post mortem was carried out by the 28-year-old Professor of Materia Medica in University College Cork, Dr Charles Yelverton Pearson.

Despite the weather having been intensely hot in the period of burial, the body was extremely well preserved. Within days, Pearson reported the finding of arsenic in large quantities in the liver, spleen and kidneys. A small amount of strychnine was found in her stomach. There was no evidence of typhoid fever. It transpired that Cross had bought a pound of arsenic for sheep-dipping in Goulding's, in September1886. He later stated that this would be an appropriate amount for 50 sheep and he had 48.

Here then, was a doctor who had purchased arsenic, seduced the governess and married her 14 days after his wife's death in suspicious circumstances. Cross was duly arrested. Crucially, the jury had to be satisfied that Laura died from arsenic poisoning and that the poison was administered by her husband.

Pearson's evidence was central to the prosecution case. He proved a formidable witness. When asked by defence council, "Dr Pearson have you ever, in your life, had to test the body of a human being for poisoning?" he replied that it was his custom to poison an animal every year and make the students test the tissues for arsenic. He then gave a comprehensive account of the available technical processes available to determine the presence of arsenic in tissue and detailed the toxic amounts he had found in the tissue of the corpse. He pointed out the remarkable preservation of the body – a feature found in arsenic poisoning. He produced actual particles of arsenious oxide that he had removed from the lining of the oesophagus.

The defence limited itself to a single witness, Dr Cross's sister, who lived in the family home. She admitted, under cross examination, to have disposed of two glass bottles containing white powder. The defence implied that Laura herself may have taken arsenic to improve her complexion. Alternatively, someone other than Dr Cross may have given it to her. They suggested that the small amount of strychnine found in her stomach might have been the result of her taking medications prescribed for her daughters.

Lord Justice Murphy, in an address lasting over four hours, repeatedly commented adversely on Cross's behaviour towards Laura. He referred to Effie as "Skinner" or "that creature", becoming deeply emotional at these times. "Ask yourselves, was Mary Laura Cross done to death by poison? If you believe she was, you must find the prisoner guilty," he concluded.

The jury deliberated for 50 minutes and delivered a guilty verdict. Cross made a defiant speech from the dock, protesting his innocence. Unusually for the time, the Lord Lieutenant did not grant a reprieve. James Berry was brought from England as the hangman. When he placed the noose around his neck, Cross refused to face the wall. Ultimately, he was allowed to face his supporters and attendant clergymen before the bolt was drawn. Berry recalled that, "of all the men I hanged, Cross was the only one who walked firmly."

Cross was executed on 10 January 1888.

Dr Pearson presented a paper entitled "The Medico-Legal Aspects of the Coachford Poisoning Case", to the Royal Academy of Medicine in Dublin three weeks after the execution. Effie delivered her son from the union a week after the trial commenced. She later left Cork and married a Londoner, with whom she had a daughter. She died of kidney cancer in 1937, at the age of 72.

While there is little doubt about his guilt, it is clear that Dr Cross's defence was poor in the extreme. His lawyers called only one witness in his defence – his sister. Lord Justice Murphy was quite emotional during the trial and in his summing up. Such conduct by a Judge would not be acceptable today. Effie seems to have been blameless in the affair, being convinced that Laura had a naturally occurring, life-threatening illness. She appears to have been completely unaware of her new husband's involvement in his first wife's death.

Further Reading
Murder at Shandy Hall: The Coachford Poisoning Case by Michael Sheridan (Poolbeg. 2010)